C000182889

To Callan and Alfie,

ZOO VET

few wishes,

MC

First published July 2007 by Shaffron Publishing Ltd
64 Hallfield Road, Layerthorpe, York   YO31 7ZQ

ISBN   978 0 955615 50 4

Cover illustration by Martin Pope (www.martinpope.co.uk)
Cover design by Clare Brayshaw

Prepared and printed by:
York Publishing Services Ltd
Tel: 01904 431213 Website: www.yps-publishing.co.uk

ZOO VET

Matt Brash

SHAFFRON
Publishing

This book is for Clare.

In a world of uncertainties, she is my rock on which I base everything.

(and boys, if I ever write another, that one can be for you, so stop complaining, you'll get one

... in the end).

Foreword

This book has evolved over a long period of time. It has finally arrived as a result of the nagging of lots of people, saying "just get on with it", and a big coincidence.

Although many people have said I should write a book, because I am completely incapable of stringing a decent English sentence together, fear has stopped me. That is until I met Cathi's rhea.

When I say rhea, I mean the bird rather than the bottom, though I am sure her rear is fine. Cathi Poole is a client whose bird became ill one day. I went out to see it, to find it recumbent on the floor and steadfastly refusing to stand. Rheas are ratites, and are related to ostriches. They are desperately inquisitive, in fact they spend their lives just being nosey. Whenever I come across a ratite lying on the ground feeling miserable, a foreign object stuck in their guts is always at the top of my list.

I told Cathi that she would need to bring her bird in for me to check over properly and X-ray, so the following day she arrived with her bird bundled up in the boot of her mini. At least it wasn't on the back of a bike. The X-ray showed there was no lump of something-that-shouldn't-be-there in its stomach, so

I took some blood samples. The blood was thin and watery looking, which meant the bird was anaemic.

My nurse and I found the underlying reason for the anaemia at almost the same time, crawling up our arms. Cathi's rhea had lice. Not just any old little louse, but ratite lice. These enormous blood-sucking beasties are quite vile and will quite literally suck the life out of a bird. They made us feel very itchy.

Fortunately they're very easy to treat. So, with the bird on medication, confident of recovery I sent it home, with Cathi, obviously. Wanting to make sure that there were no other problems, I also sent the blood off for analysis. Two days later the results returned, and so I rang the phone number Cathi had left me.

This telephone call kick-started my career as an author. It was late in the evening, and I was tired. The conversation went something like this.

"Hullo."

"Oh, hello. Is Cathi there?"

"No."

"Oh. I was just ringing to talk about Cathi's rhea."

"What's wrong with her rear? It looked fine to me this morning."

"No, her rhea."

"Oh, her ear. Are you a doctor?"

Slightly put out, I decided to try a different tactic.

"I'm sorry, who am I talking to?"

"Duncan, from Shaffron Publishing."

"Shaffron Publishing? Ooooh. I've been meaning to write a book."

"Really."

"Yes. Can you help?"

"Cathi said you should be writing a book. You had better come and see me."

So I forgot all about the rhea and went home excitedly to tell the family that we were going to write a book. So thanks Cathi, thanks Duncan and most of all thanks to Cathi's rhea, without all three of which there would never have been a book.

There are a million other people who I should thank for all their support, not only in writing this book but also in helping me with my career as a zoo vet. They all know who they are, and many thanks to them. The list is too long and would become boring.

But I must thank two special animals. The first is Guilty, our dog, who has sat in her basket patiently watching me type through the long hours of early mornings. I know exactly what she's been thinking, as she has lain there in her basket with her big brown eyes never leaving my face: 'Less typing, bozo and more walkies'.

The second is Jojo, our cockatoo. Jojo has sat on my shoulder, my arm and even my fingers, desperate to help the progress of this book. He has, throughout the evolution of this tome, developed new levels of self-control that he never knew he had, the best being resisting the temptation to pull all the keys off my laptop. I've had to type on a laptop because he has already pulled most of the keys off the house computer. I've tried putting them back, but I think I've got them in the wrong order: typing is now like eating a box of chocolates, you never quite know what you are going to get!

Chapter One

"Bugger, it stood up! It actually just stood up, 500 kilos of angry animal and me in a small enclosure. Not funny at all!"

I was telling a story about a polar bear anaesthetic that hadn't gone entirely to plan, to a TV producer called Katie Metcalfe. We were sitting in a cheap chippy in Scarborough sipping coffee and she had asked what sort of work I did. This sort of dramatic, yet slightly run-of-the-mill, event seemed to encapsulate everything I did in a nut shell.

It was very large. A 500-kilo polar bear, belonging to Flamingo Land Zoo, that was one of a pair of twins that had been born to proud parents Mandy and Marcus. When the bears were three years old their parents had had enough of them, as one does when one's child is three. A home had been found for them at another zoo. My job was to anaesthetise them so that they could be loaded onto a crate ready for transport. It all sounded fairly easy in theory. However, the problem was that the bear enclosure was ideal for the beasts to reside in, but it wasn't that great to get them out of. There were two parts, an outside area with a pool and a large pit filled with bark chippings and some housing. The housing was made up of a series of rooms that mimicked a cave. Here the bears spent their winters, so it was small and dark and cosy. Each room was about three metres by three metres and only about one and a half metres high. This would be bedded out thickly with straw in the winter, providing the bears with the ideal environment to snooze their way through the long winter nights. The only light was a smidgen of daylight that trickled through a little grill in the metal door. The bears had no need for any artificial lighting, so when we looked in we blocked out all the illumination. Bizarrely, I needed a second person to hold a torch over my shoulder so I that could actually locate 500 kilos of snow-white polar bear.

Neville, the Zoo's headkeeper, shone the torch while I stuck the barrel of my dart gun through the grill. At the appropriate moment, when the bear was sitting still long enough, I would fire the dart and hopefully it would hit the right place, his bottom, so that the anaesthetic could take effect more efficiently. Polar bears aren't daft, and this one knew exactly who I was, and so sat there, buttocks firmly pressed into the corner. He had a knowing look on his face punctuated by a sinister snarl and a low rumbling growl that echoed round the building. Not only would he not present the target for me, but the bear weighed so much that it was going to take three darts to get him asleep. The first, I knew, would really tick him off, and that's when I expected him to charge the door, roaring and bellowing bad bear breath in my face. Trust me, bear breath is worse than dog breath, and there's a lot more of it.

Neville shone the torch, I pointed the gun – Bang! Bang! Bang! – three darts found their target. After darting any animal, we always wait a good 20 minutes to make sure it is fully asleep before going in. But how to know that an animal is really asleep is always the tricky part. This is when the adrenaline starts pumping. At some point somebody's got to go in and make sure the animal is asleep, and for some odd reason zookeepers always feel that, in their opinion, the vet is the most expendable and should go in first.

So how do you check an animal is really sound asleep? We always try drain rods; the type you use for clearing a blocked drain. Minus the brush, we push the rods through one by one, connecting them as they go. Finally, when we reach the animal, we poke it; no reaction means it is anaesthetised. It sounds comical, but it's usually quite an exact science and, in the case of the polar bear, it seemed to work; the beast was asleep.

The next step was to go in and have a look. Usually I did this armed to the teeth with a broom. A broom!? In my heart of hearts I knew that if the bear was awake a broom would be pretty ineffective. In fact, he'd probably use it as a tooth pick after he'd finished with me, but at times like this a broom is a vet's best friend. It's just one of those tools that has passed down in the mists of zoo folklore. A bit like hanging onto a rope when one is falling into an abyss.

Neville opened the door and, bending double, I crept in. A couple of taps on his shoulder with the broom got no response at all, so I called the others in. The next step was to bind his muzzle with some sticky tape. Again it sounds comical, but 'sticky-backed plastic' is as useful to a vet as it is to a *Blue Peter* presenter. It meant he wouldn't be able to bite me if everything went wrong.

He was lying facing the wrong way, towards the wall, so to get him out we would have to turn him over. We brought a large tarpaulin in and laid it out on the ground. When everything was ready, we would roll him over onto the tarpaulin and drag him out to the waiting lorry.

Imagine the scene: there were six of us in this small, dark, damp room. Neville was holding his torch as high as he could.

I was sitting holding the bear's head, taping up the jaws. We were nervously silent, which made the low, guttural grumbling sounds emanating from the bear all the more spine chilling. I placed four people around him, one on each leg, and asked Neville to edge back towards the door but keep the lighting where we needed it. The hot, fetid smell of bear was rampant and the complete lack of good visibility and room was making co-ordinated movements tricky.

"Right everyone," I said, taking command, "I will count one, two, three, and we'll roll him over. OK?"

Everyone grunted; we were all set.

I counted and said, "Roll."

We rolled him over, and he stood up!

Well, I have never moved so fast in my entire life. Or at least tried to, in the cramped, panic-stricken room. The six of us charged at the small door, trying to squeeze our way through it all at the same time. As the person who had been holding his head, I was going to be last. We scrambled our way out through the door, not turning to see what was happening behind us. I was just waiting for the thump of the massive paws landing on my back. What was probably only seconds seemed like hours. As I passed through the door last, I slammed it shut and hurtled down the corridor after the others. Once we were all outside, we slammed the secondary security doors shut as well.

There we stopped, caught our breath, looked nervously at each other to check we were all there, then burst into laughter. Everybody was OK, although we were all a tad greyer for the experience. Still, that's zoo work, unpredictable at the best of times. We did what all good zookeepers do at times like this, and had a cigarette.

A few minutes later we opened the outer doors to the corridor. No sign of a large bear in there, so we crept back down to have a look in his den. He hadn't gone far; all he had done was get up and fall over again. We repeated the process with the drain rods, then with the broom and, once I was fully confident (again! sheesh!) that he was asleep, I went back in. This time he stayed down and the procedure went without a hitch, and off he went to his new home.

"So that's what I do," I said to Katie. "Fun, eh?"

Katie sat there grinning and sipping her coffee.

"This we have to film," she replied.

Katie Metcalfe was a producer working for Real Life Media Productions, who I had met for the first time that day. Now she was talking about filming me. I was going to add that it wasn't always as dramatic as this, but thought that might burst her bubble, so I didn't.

So really all my TV work has came about totally by accident.

The year was 1998, when I first met Katie; I had been asked to take part in a raid on a suspected parrot smuggler in Scarborough. Coincidentally, it was also being filmed for a TV series called *Wildlife Police* and that was why Katie was there. It was a show that dealt with animal-related crime. The RSPCA, together with Customs & Excise, were on the trail of a suspected parrot smuggler. Yes, parrot smuggling does rather conjure up images of Monty Python, but there are serious issues to take into account, such as the import and spread of tropical diseases and the welfare of the smuggled birds. This is potentially big business, with some rare parrots, such as the Lear's macaw, being worth tens of thousands of pounds.

The raid was on a Scarborough parrot owner who was alleged to have two Emma's conures (a breed of small parrot) that had been brought into the country in order to complete his, otherwise immaculately kept, collection. A bit like getting hold of the two missing stamps for your philately collection. Or that elusive 1965 Beatle's 7-inch single mispressing of *Day Tripper*. Or something.

The RSPCA had asked me to go along, as I had helped them with lots of undercover cloak and dagger work before, mainly associated with badger baiting. I was there to ensure the parrots weren't stressed and were in good health. On the way up to Scarborough, I had started thinking that if this chap had a massive collection of parrots how on earth would I identify the smuggled birds. I'm not a parrot-ist so I'd obviously have to wing it (sorry!).

Before the raid, we were waiting in a local police station while everyone got organised. We were all to be briefed about the forthcoming events and were gathered together in a large room sitting in a circle. There were police officers, RSPCA officers, representatives from the Parrot Society, a film crew and myself. It all seemed very serious and daunting to me.

I began to suspect the police were sensing my naivety and were keen to have some fun at the expense of this 'poncy southern vet', particularly as the cameras were there. The sergeant in charge, a large burly fellow, with a barrel chest and a deep booming voice, had a positive glint in his eye as he went through the procedures and the worst that could happen in this kind of situation. Good old health and safety, it comes into play even in a raid on a potential smuggler. He bandied about blood-curdling scenarios in which the defendant may lash out with guns, axes, flame-throwers, bombs, you name it. I must admit, I was rather having second thoughts about the whole situation, which must have been obvious judging by the smug smirks and wicked grins from the rest of the assembled police.

But, vets are rarely beaten and, when the opportunity arose for a small slice of revenge, I took it with both trembling hands. Once the boys in blue and everyone else had finished having their say, the burly sergeant turned to me and asked:

"Now young vet'nary, have you got anything you wish to add?"

"Yes, thank you," I said. "There are a whole bunch of potential bugs that we can catch from birds, but there is a particularly tricky one that you can catch from parrots, called *Chlamydia*. This one is particularly nasty. In the bird the disease it causes is known as psittacosis. The birds may show no symptoms at all, but can shed the bug in their poo or in the air. It is easily transmitted to humans, where it is called ornithosis. In man it is potentially rather dangerous."

"Ow nasty are we talking?" asked the now distracted Sergeant. Indeed, all his men had become quite stern of face and were listening hard.

"Flu like symptoms, usually," I said, to which they collectively breathed a sigh of relief. A short one, because then I added, "Then death."

At that I stood up, clapped my hands and suggested we get cracking.

"Oh and by the way," I added, "they can also transmit *E. coli*, *Salmonella* and *Campylobacter*, but they only cause the runs."

They rose slowly, and it was my turn to smirk. I was going to guild the lily and add that the assembled officers now looked as sick as parrots, but in retrospect I'm glad I didn't. When bluffing, a little is more than enough, which is why I didn't tell them that human mortality as a result of *Chlamydia* is less than 1%.

All the talk before the raid had taken so long that, by the time we finally arrived at the suspect's premises he had gone out. So we were dispatched to have an early lunch while the police went off around Scarborough to try and track down their man.

This was how I found myself sitting down next to Katie Metcalfe, a producer from Real Life Media Productions, telling ever taller tales about my work at Flamingo Land. I was flattered she wanted to film my work, but I really had no idea of the long and winding road it would take me down.

The raid went as planned and without any violent incident when the terrified-looking suspect returned from his lunch to be met by a crowd of uniformed officers. He was a quiet, shy man and obviously very distressed by the whole affair. The police issued him with a search warrant and entered his premises. At no point did I see any knives or shotguns, let alone flame-throwers. Inside the building, an old converted garage by the look of it, it was all very neat. Downstairs he had row upon row of dustbins where he was busy researching what he considered the perfect diet for a parrot. Upstairs he had a large collection of amazing parrots, quite beautifully kept. All of this carefully hidden away in a back street of Scarborough.

He was a nice chap, as it happens. Completely the opposite of what you'd think a smuggler would be like. He didn't even have one of the parrots on his shoulder! I have always enjoyed meeting such people; experts in their own field, and I could listen to them for hours. Certainly one of the great things about working with exotic animals is the fact that you never stop learning things.

A representative of the Parrot Society positively identified the suspect birds. How, I don't know, as I have to say that, staring at all those conures, they all looked identical to me. The process of the identification was the longest part of the operation, and the experts spent hours pouring over books to ensure that they had got the correct birds. The ones we were after were a type of subtype of conure, of which there are six subtypes in total. That's the beauty of a well-practised and expert eye, like the one I don't have, so I left them to it. I wandered back downstairs to find the suspect sitting disconsolately on his bins full of bird seed.

"Are you alright?"

"Not really," he replied, "You're that new bird vet from Malton aren't you?"

I replied in the affirmative and we struck up a conversation, chatting about the pros and cons of feeding seed to parrots. He had been researching different ways to balance different seeds to create a diet that would both provide good food and an interesting diet. A few minutes later he no longer seemed bothered about all the goings on upstairs, as he was deeply entrenched in explaining his work to me. Finally all the experts came back downstairs, having satisfied themselves that they had got their birds. I examined the two parrots and found them to be in the rudest of health, with no evidence of disease. This came as a relief to the police officers, who had remained pale throughout the whole investigation. Thankfully, since then, I've haven't had much dealing with these innocent and impressionable creatures. Parrots, on the other hand, and TV crews, have kept me busy ever since.

I don't know whether they ever found out whether the suspect had smuggled the birds in or not, but he has stayed a good friend and client ever since.

Chapter Two

But hold on, perhaps I'm getting ahead of myself. I really ought to explain how I got from vet school to becoming the vet for Flamingo Land Zoo, in North Yorkshire, and to raiding suspect parrot smugglers in Scarborough.

I first became the vet for Flamingo Land Zoo, just near Pickering, way back in 1991, and it was soon after I had started that I had had my dramatic run in with a polar bear.

If you've never been to the Zoo, go! My kids love it, and not just because Dad has now been the vet there for nearly 17 years. It is genuinely an amazing place for a fun family day out. There are large parts of the park where I have never even been. Apart from the Zoo, there are the most hideous scary rides that quite honestly just make me want to throw up. But again my kids love them. Fortunately I am getting to that age when the fear of having a heart attack provides me with a sufficient excuse not to go on the really big ones. To be honest, I prefer the Zoo itself, which is chock-full of more than 400 various types of animals. You may have to look hard to see some of them, but that's deliberate. The Zoo is constantly developing, and more and more sophisticated enclosures have been built to provide the animals with a stimulating and complex environment in which to live. They are all lovingly looked after by the expert staff. And that's no mean feat, as we are talking rhinos, giraffes, camels, antelopes, big cats, vultures, penguins, exotic birds, reptiles, fish, right through to insects. And a lot more.

I think this is a good point to just say a few words about zoos in general. I do not plan to preach, just to say what I think about zoos. No one likes a bad zoo, and I couldn't agree more. But a good zoo is vitally important. In this day and age doubly so, when so many species of our wild animals are disappearing. All zoos assist in the education of the public, as well as in conservation and research. Not all of us can afford to go on safari to Africa to see the majesty of a lion, or the rumble of a rhino as it runs, so zoos provide a safe environment for children to see the animals that make up this wonderful planet of ours. The memories will stay with them throughout their entire life. I clearly remember my father taking me to a zoo as a child and holding me up to see the lions. After me, he held our dog up to say hullo to the lion and got peed on down his shirt for his troubles.

So a good zoo is important. Behind the scenes, rare animals are bred as part of global breeding programmes called EEPs. Students spend hours with clipboards studying animal behaviour and developing ways of enhancing their lives. The animals that is, not the students. Much of this research filters its way into world-wide zoo publications, and each little piece of the puzzle may prove helpful in eventually saving some animal somewhere.

Flamingo Land is a superb zoo and has events going on all year round. Think of it as an animal hotel, a five-star Dorchester job in which all the residents are pampered and loved.

They do, however, have one other thing in common, none of them like me. It's not my aftershave or my sense of humour, they object to. It's because, even though I'm there to help and heal, they see me as 'that bloke who sticks needles in us'. Most of them walk cautiously away as soon as they spot me, but some, like Nelson the chimp, would dearly love to kill me and would, given half a chance, in as gory a way as possible.

I trained at the Royal Veterinary College in London. It is one of the oldest veterinary schools of the seven in the UK, and is based in Camden Town, with a field station in Hertfordshire, near Potters Bar.

Whilst there, I met Clare, in 1984. I was two years older, still am funnily enough, and so was two years ahead of her, in my third year of a five-year course: that's the maths bit out of the way! Two years later I qualified and moved to my first job in Winchester. So whilst she was still entrenched in the life of the carefree partying student, I'd kind of got over all that and was developing a keen interest in growing vegetables. I even had a pair of slippers and a favourite chair by that time, trundling at a steady pace towards old fartdom. I suppose the politically correct term would be 'youthfully challenged' or maybe 'boringly gifted'. So, as she partied, I was a serious, qualified vet with a passion for purple-sprouting broccoli and the different techniques of repairing broken ligaments. I had no hope of keeping such a vibrant, enthusiastic young thing as a girlfriend and so I became, temporarily, a thing of her past.

We remained very close friends however, and, yet another two years later, Clare, now also a qualified vet, rang me in a panic as she was about to start her very first job in Yorkshire. So I quickly packed my slippers, waved goodbye to my favourite chair and broccoli, and set off for a weekend in Yorkshire to offer some moral support. When I got there, she'd completely got over her panic attack and said "I'm fine now". Why she couldn't have done that over the phone, I still don't know, but thank God she didn't as I was falling in love again, and not just with the Yorkshire countryside.

Clare's a brilliant equestrian vet, that's horse boffin to the rest of us. She took me round the wolds surrounding Malton, for ham, egg and chips in the Cross Keys pub in Thixendale, and long walks on the moors. We had such a heavenly time together, I drove home on the Monday and promptly handed in my notice and put my house up for sale. I knew I'd found the girl and the place of my dreams to live, now I just needed a job.

I had two interviews for a new job. The first practice I visited was way up on the moors. Breathtakingly lovely. We drove round visiting some of their clients and I was blown away by the empty roads and the way nothing had changed since James Herriot's time. On one farm, an elderly farmer proudly showed us his farmyard that had just been concreted for the first time ever. There were tiny farms with just a handful of animals. It was so very far away from the high-tech big farms down south, where animals were just numbers and not Mabel and June. The farmers still handed my prospective employer a bucket of icy-cold water, a bar of soap and a towel when he had finished his job. On one farm, they even washed down his boots with the hose! I was stunned. I had enjoyed my life in Winchester and all the people I had met, but this was more real and what I was coming north for. However, I hesitated. It's strange what can sway the course of one's life so dramatically, but I remember having reservations about the practice. The principal, a 40-year-old, used saucers with his teacups, an odd thing to remember I know, but it struck me that we were not compatible simply because of that. Also, he had a beard, which Clare always distrusts for some odd reason. There must have been better reasons but they have been lost in the mists of time.

Soon after, an offer came up in Beverley. I was lucky enough to get an interview and be offered the job with the Peel Vet Group. I joined them in the January of 1991. It too was a lovely practice, just outside North Bar Without, and my boss was a delightful man called Keith Dobson. I was only there for nine months, but they were really some of the happiest times of my life as a bachelor. The work was easy, everyone was so laid back and friendly, it was a fabulous welcome to the north of England and a real eye-opener to what 'quality of life' actually meant. An average working day would be finished by about 10 in the morning. Keith would go off and play golf and I was left to run the practice. (Sorry to let the cat out of the bag, Keith.) We managed to increase work by about 300% in the nine months I was there but, even so, I did feel that perhaps this wasn't going anywhere long term.

Fortunately, towards the end of that year, I was offered an interview at The Mount Vet Group in Malton, and it was whilst I was having my interview there that they asked me if I would be interested in doing the Zoo. I had been brought up with exotic animals, and thought how hard could this really be, so immediately jumped at the chance and said "Yes".

I joined The Mount, starting on the Monday, at the same time as Andrew Forsyth, a dry-witted, charming Scot who had just qualified from the Glasgow Vet School. He told me he'd been the first and only vet in Scotland to breed haggis successfully in captivity. I now know he was pulling my leg; it's actually *never* been done. I'm not daft!

He and I became good friends and still work together 17 years later. Those were fun days too. Andrew and I worked a one in two rota, i.e. we would work one weekend then have the next one off. What always impressed me about him was that, when I was on duty, he used to go off either mountaineering or training with his territorial regiment. On the Monday, I would always feel exhausted, having spent the weekend sitting waiting for telephone calls in the middle of the night, and perhaps had the odd call out to a farm to calve a cow or look at a sneezing rabbit. Andrew, however, would have driven up to the top of Scotland on the Friday evening, leapt out of a plane and walked 300 miles carrying at least 80 kilos on his back. He always looked as fresh as a daisy of a Monday morning, even though he had only had about two hours sleep. Ah well, I took consolation in the knowledge that I grew much better vegetables. Clare, however, used to visit me at the surgery much more frequently, as she used to try and time her visits to when Andrew went on his nearly topless runs every afternoon.

Within my first week I was to encounter the truly unique phenomenon called the Yorkshire farmer. They are well known for their canniness, and James Herriot made them famous for how unwilling they are to part with their brass.

Mr Harrison was standing at the reception desk, his omnipresent flat-cap was on and his pipe smouldered in the corner of his mouth.

Stevie, our receptionist, called me over and said would I mind helping as she was slightly confused about what he was asking for.

"Now then, Mr Harrison, how are you?"

"Fair to middling, young veterinary," came the fairly stock Yorkshire farmer reply.

I asked him how I could help, and he told me that one of his sows had cut her shoulder on a nail. Upon inquiring further he told me that the wound wasn't that big, "about an inch'n"alf".

I explained exactly what he would need to close the wound. Local anaesthetic, suture equipment, cutting needles, special suture material, then antibiotics and painkillers.

He thought for a bit, chewing on the stem of his pipe.

"Aye, this sounds jolly complicated to me," said Mr Harrison, "will it cost me a fortune for you to come and do it?"

"Only about and inch and a half you said? Well, I won't take very long, maybe 10 minutes, shall we call that 10 or 15 pounds?"

"Aye, OK, well you can come and do it then," he said. His bright eyes twinkled from behind the pipe smoke. I should have smelt a rat.

That evening, I took the old Roman road up above Settrington, to his farm miles from anywhere in the midst of the wolds. It was a beautiful evening and from the top of Settrington the view is quite stunning, as you look across Ryedale towards the moors in the distance.

On arrival, I was greeted with, "You're late."

This seemed harsh, as I hadn't said when I would be there, but these things aren't worth worrying about. Having made his point, and successfully wrong-footing me, he took me through to one of the old converted sheep pens and there stood a large sow.

"She's me prize sow," he said, "so you'd best do a proper job."

She was facing away from me, so I turned and said, "So where exactly is the wound?"

"On her shoulder."

At this point the sow turned round and there was the wound. Sure enough it was approximately one and a half inches ... wide!! And about two foot long.

"Now don't forget, you said it would only be 10 to 15 pounds in total."

He settled himself comfortably against the wall, and got out his matches to relight his pipe. I cursed and realised that I had been had, but an agreement was an agreement.

"Will you be able to help me?"

"Nay lad, I'm far too old to be tackling pigs, you'll be on your own in there, but I'll stay and watch if you like."

I climbed into the pig pen; she was a quiet girl, which made my life easier, and I managed to get a local anaesthetic in and set to stitching the wound up. Occasionally she would get bored and wander off, leaving me to trail after her with my instruments flying. After an hour I finally finished, and stood back proudly looking at my handy work. It was a good job. I gave her some long-acting antibiotics, a bit of painkiller and left instructions for Mr Harrison to take the stitches out in about two weeks time. The whole episode had taken a good two hours in total.

A month later, Mr Harrison was back at the surgery; he was standing there, holding a yellow piece of paper, arguing with Stevie. Stevie called me over,

"I think you'd better come and help, he's very angry."

I walked over, "Hello, Mr Harrison, how did that pig do?"

"Aye, well, not too bad, it's your bill I've come to complain about."

"Yes, Mr Harrison, what seems to be the trouble? I did exactly as we agreed, I've only charged you 10 pounds for sewing her up, and I was there for two hours, and a few drugs."

"Aye, but you never said anything about a bloody visit fee."

Welcome to Yorkshire; Herriot had written about them quite accurately.

We managed to stay friends over the issue and, years later Mr Harrison's son David became godfather to our first son Jack.

I soon settled into my new life and began to find my way around. It was a lovely practice, and I enjoyed meeting a whole set of new faces. Although most of our work was with farm and small animals, I was looking forward to my first visit to the Zoo.

I was unsure exactly what to expect. On that first visit, I drove the seven miles from Malton to Kirby Misperton nervously, wondering whether I would be any good at this.

At the big main gates, I stopped and announced that I was the new vet. The man on the gate looked at me slowly and waved me through. Go to the keepers' yard he said. I wandered around the Zoo for a while, until I stumbled across an official-looking man who took me to the right place.

"Here you are mate," he said.

There I was met by Neville, a wizened nut-brown wrinkled Yorkshire man, with a keen dry sense of humour and a very phlegmatic sense of life and death. My duties, he told me, would be to walk round the Zoo and check every animal. At the time I was staring at a rather large North American bison, who was gently pawing at the ground, almost daring me to come in there and check him over. Neville's knowledge of zoo animals, the zoo world and zoo vets in particular was encyclopaedic. He had seen them all come and go, and he could relate marvellous tales of what things had been like in the 1960s.

As we walked round the Zoo on that first day, I warmed to him. I finally decided to open up to him.

"I've never looked after a zoo before."

"Oh, I shouldn't worry," he said, "neither had any of your predecessors."

He went on to add:

"We once had a vet who got it so badly wrong that he nearly killed one of the chimpanzees. We thought about suing him, but our lawyer told us that no-one had ever successfully sued a zoo vet before."

I took a lot of courage from this phlegmatic statement. I wasn't entirely sure what he was trying to tell me, but I presumed his expectations weren't high. He was a very kind man and, by the end of our walk round, I felt like I had known him all my life. There was no doubt that he would guide me in my dealings with these big animals and, provided I listened to him, I should stay on the right side of the lawyers.

So he was the man I thought of immediately when the Yorkshire police rang one afternoon to say that a lion had been spotted walking into a wood at Ruston Parva. They were unsure whether it was a lion or a lioness, but of one thing they were sure, it was definitely a lion. A lion! None had been reported missing and, come on, you'd notice if you lost one of them, surely; so I was a tad sceptical, but you never know.

Neville was the man I needed, he was a brilliant shot with the rifle as well as having unbounded knowledge of lions and tigers.

I picked up the phone and rang:

"Neville, I need you, there's an escaped lion down at Ruston Parva, it's been spotted crossing a field and going into a wood, can you come and give us a hand?"

"Aye," was the dulcet reply.

I drove up and collected him and his guns, and we headed off. There was silence in the car as we both thought about the job that lay ahead.

Suddenly Neville turned to me and said:

"I ain't going into no bloody wood with a lion."

Good point, I thought.

We went back to a stony silence.

On arriving, it was apparent that the police had turned out in force. There were large numbers of local bobbies, armed response teams, SWAT and even the chief constable had arrived. He had decided that a search of the whole area was critical, so had ordered a helicopter to come from the Coastguard. Neville was to go up in the helicopter and scout around looking for any signs, whilst I interviewed the families that had seen the lion. Neville seemed happier at this prospect as, being in a helicopter, he would be safe.

There were two small, stone bungalows set back into a hill with a wonderful view across the valley in front of them. Each family had seen the lion come out of the top of the wood on the far valley, cross down in front of some fields and then head into another wood. Both sets of families were absolutely adamant that it was a lioness. I started to interview the first family. The mother explained how it was the children who had first seen the lioness at seven o'clock that morning. She went on to say that, after leaving the wood, as it had passed a small shrub in the field, it had stopped, cocked its leg, had a pee and moved on.

A flickering of understanding crossed my mind and I began to giggle to myself. As everybody knows, of course, lions are just big pussy cats and so don't cock their legs. I went to interview the second family, and they related the same tale, how the lion had come down from the woods, crossed the field, cocked its leg, and then gone on to the next woods.

I wondered about the best way to break the news to the chief of police, as he now had more than 200 officers in attendance and was getting ready to beat through the woods to try and track the lion down. He may not take it well, but I felt it was my duty to tell them.

"Sir," I said, calling him gently to one side. "I think you ought to know that I really don't think this is going to be a lion; in fact, I can be 100% sure it's not a lion. The animal in question cocked its leg as it crossed the field. It's just a large dog."

The chief constable stopped and thought for a while. He looked at his watch, with studied concentration.

"My goodness me, it's quarter to twelve, it must be lunch time; I must arrange for a lunch cart to arrive. Then we'll think of something to do with the boys after lunch."

He went to leave, but turned back, "Don't say a word," he said.

We sat down to a rather good three-course lunch courtesy of the police mobile canteen. As soon as it was over, he called his troops together. He had sworn me to secrecy and I stood beside him as he passed out his orders. They were directed to make a search of the quarry; so, placing his SWAT team on the high ground, he sent the obviously more expendable local bobbies into the disused quarry.

I could see the fear on their faces as they set off, thinking that at any minute they might stumble upon a rather pissed-off lion. I stood there biting my lip, and trying not to laugh. Working with the police was fun.

Luckily, none was ever found. Neville had a great trip in a helicopter and neither of us ever had to walk into that wood to look for the lion.

Although nationally there have been thousands of sightings of big cats since then, sadly I have never been needed by the police for one again. Perhaps it's because they would rather not know so early on it is a dog. Certainly, I personally have always been a bit of a sceptic. It would not be easy for a lion to hide in the English countryside.

Clare and I finally married in 1992. Now she weeds my broccoli and nicks my favourite armchair!

Chapter Three

I think if I dismissed our wedding in just one line I would be crucified by Clare. It was, after all, a great event, and there are a few little bits and pieces that are worth recounting here. Clare hails from Lincolnshire, in a small village near Louth, and this was where we married.

I had very little say in the whole matter, which really suited me just fine. Clare's parents initially said it would have to be a small affair, and quite honestly we were happy with that. I was put in charge of just three things, the beer, the band and my car. I was to fail miserably regarding all three.

The beer should have been easy, but I didn't really know where to start. How many barrels, what type, and when to get them? Fortunately Clare's brother knew all the local hostelries and was able to organise several barrels of beer. As I had been banned from the premises for the week before the great day, I wasn't even able to go and get them. Clare's brother kindly did so, and even went to the trouble of sampling the ale to make sure it was up to scratch.

Organising the band was just as problematic. I know very little about music. Genesis, the Beatles and Supertramp were my thing at school, then Bob Marley and Chris de Burgh at college, but how to book any of these acts was beyond me. Anyway, I think Bob Marley's dead and I'm pretty sure the Beatles have broken up.

When I was first put in charge of the music, I rang various agents in the Yellow Pages. They were all very helpful, advising me that if I was to go Manchester the following Friday I would be able to listen to the Blurbs playing in such-and-such a nightclub between one a.m. and three. This just was not my thing, a good book and tea is all that is needed after 10 o'clock. The thought of trailing around Manchester's nightclubs on a Friday night panicked me.

I decide to ring Clare's father and confess.

"Help, I really don't know what I'm doing," I explained.

"Mmm. Would you like me to have a try?" He must have heard my nodding and sighs of relief down the phone, as he followed quickly with, "Leave it with me."

Within a week he rang back to say he had found a rather good jazz band, would that do? How did he do that? Would that do?! It sounded perfect, as we have both always adored jazz.

"The band is a four-piece with a singer," he went on, "And they will play all afternoon and evening."

It all sounded just perfect.

Two weeks before the great day, he rang back.

"There is good news," he said. "The band has rung, and if we have the space then the rest of the band would like to come and play as well." This sounded great.

"How many?"

"Twenty-four and four singers."

Wow. That's a lot of jazz musicians, I thought. I wondered if they were all necessary and if some were wedding crashers just posing as jazz musicians. But, it sounded like a lot of fun, so I said the more the merrier.

The last thing I was left in charge of was my car. Ooops.

They had all told me that under no circumstance was I to bring my car anywhere near the wedding. But, you know, I knew best.

We were married at four p.m., in a small country church into which we crammed a colossal number of guests who had lovingly decorated the place just for us. The organist was an old family friend, and the vicar was my old house master from school, Canon Peter Allen. So much for a small wedding. My best man, Paul Allen, affectionately known as Pegleg, was an ex-marine who had lost his foot in the Falklands war. He's the only person I know who could effectively steal from a shoe shop.

Pegleg had lived with us at college for several years and had long ago been made an honorary vet. We were ready by lunchtime and had a few hours to kill, and so he took me to the pub. There we were joined by lots of mates from college and, of course, family and friends.

After a few pints, it was time to go. Paul offered to drive, which was a relief, after three pints. It's never been good form to end up in the nick for drink driving. Especially not on one's wedding day. Paul took the wheel and parked the car for me at the church.

I stood nervously in the churchyard greeting people as they arrived. Funny how you can never remember even one's own parents' names at a moment like that.

Clare, meanwhile, was a hundred yards down the road at her mother's house. Their leaving for the church was delayed by her mother's insistence in washing out the bath dressed in her full wedding finery. Plus she wanted to watch the 3.30 from Aintree.

They finally waltzed up the road, singing away, whilst I stood in the church in a panic. Of course the wedding ring hardly fit over her finger, because of the stress of the day, but we got there. Any thoughts of my car had long since vanished.

After the wedding came the speeches and the party. What a band, what a day!

At about 11 o'clock in the evening my new mother in-law came and found me to suggest that we went to Ireland in her brother's camper van. This had been a long-standing debate, but I was insistent that we would go in my car. I went back to supping beer and chatting to long-lost friends. Who knows, I might never see them again.

One hour later, my mother-in-law again tracked me down.

"You will have to take my car, if you won't take the van," she said. Through the thick mist of alcohol, a light began to dawn.

"What's wrong with my car," I asked, feeling for my keys. Keys that weren't there. In horror I realised that I had left them with the best man!

Ooops.

He had meant to be good, he had had the best of intentions, but as the evening had worn on his intentions had disappeared! At around 10 o'clock my college friends had pinned him down and he gave up the keys to my car, helpfully telling them where he had parked it.

After turfing the roof of the car, and filling the back seat with a pair of sheep, and smearing everything with yukky veterinary goo, they had decided, in their wisdom, to switch the accelerator cable and the brake cable. The idea being that when I accelerated, I would brake and vice versa. This was perhaps a bit ambitious, and didn't work. The cable snapped, and they didn't have a spare. They called the AA. The AA had been unable to do anything so had called the RAC. They were unable to help either.

Now it was midnight on my wedding night, and I was already faced with an angry-looking mother-in-law and an even crosser new wife!

The guests wanted us to leave, and we would not be going anywhere in my car for a while.

I know when I am a lost man, and so couldn't agree more; my mother-in-law's car was just perfect.

As we got into the back seat of the car, the driver turned and asked if we were all ready to go. Clare smiled through clenched teeth and said yes. She had known about the car problem for two hours and she was not amused.

On arriving at our hotel, the carefully arranged violinist had departed, the ice melted, and the champagne warmed. Clare climbed into bed, muttering about divorce.

Three things, that was all I had had to do! It was a good lesson, though. It taught me to just agree with everything your wife ever says, and never give your car keys to your best man. He is, after all, only there to stitch you up.

Fortunately, Clare forgave me. We had the most wonderful honeymoon in a small village on the very west coast of Ireland, called Kilbaha. The location of our honeymoon had in many ways been determined by our pets. Moving in with Clare had also meant moving in with her collection of animals. Curlew her Burmese cat couldn't come on the honeymoon, but she wasn't going anywhere without Fly. Fly was a very devoted, almost fixated, halitotic whippet. Pets that belong to people from before they are married carry a very special significance, as they are often their only link with freedom. They are pets that have been gathered after leaving home but before setting up home.

Kilbaha really was the tiniest of villages, made up of two cottages and two pubs. The cottage belonged to old, old family friends of ours who had kindly agreed to lend it to us for a fortnight. The village had not had a honeymoon couple there for years, and so welcomed us with open arms.

We had been given some advice before we went that, if we went into one pub, we should go into the other, or there would be trouble.

The cottage had been decorated to celebrate our arrival and, on opening the front door, we were welcomed by an overpowering smell of rotting fish. Ah, the true smell of Ireland, we thought to ourselves. The door to our bedroom had been decorated with the 'honeymoon couple' and on our bed, nestling on a pile of rotting kelp, were two bottles of champagne. This was where the strong smell was emanating from,

On our first evening, we popped into the first pub for a quick pint of Guinness. There we were greeted like long-lost friends, and several hours later we stumbled down the road to the second pub. By the time we had finished there we could hardly stand. The locals, however, had discovered that Clare was a racehorse vet and she had now promised to look at every broken-down nag within a hundred miles. They had also discovered I liked fishing and were determined to drag me off to the river. I later guessed this was to give Clare enough free time to do all the horse work she'd drunkenly promised to do. If we were lucky we might be reunited for supper.

It was the most blissful honeymoon and, most unlike Ireland, the sun shone all the time.

Fly enjoyed roaming across the hill sides as we walked during whatever free time we were allowed. This helped work up an appetite for our next session of Guinness.

Four days after we arrived, a small fishing boat pulled into the tiny harbour. It was the local lobster potter. I had never had lobster and was fairly certain that Clare hadn't either. It would be a great honeymoon surprise and so I purchased a large, three-pound lobster, fresh from the Atlantic. So fresh, in fact, that he still had not had his pincers banded up. I carried him back up to the cottage in a small soggy cardboard box and proudly produced supper. It would make a change from Guinness and crisps.

The cottage was incredibly old, with large stone flagged floors and low crumbling ceilings. The kitchen was simple but practical, with a solid school-like gas cooker along one wall. Fortunately it was set up to cater for large groups of people. Clare found a large cauldron in which we could cook the lobster, which we had now affectionately called 'Clickety Clack'.

You should never give something you are going to eat a name; it's mean.

Meanwhile, we made a quick trip to the payphone at the end of the village to ring England to find out how long you should cook lobster for.

We had fresh Irish bread ready on the table and opened our first bottle of champagne. We had since discovered that they had thought we were coming the week before, which was why the kelp had been left rotting.

Once the pot was boiling hard, we decided the time was ready to put poor Clickety Clack in. Neither of us wanted to hear the alleged scream, and so planned to put him in and then rush outside to drink our champagne.

I opened the soggy box and, summoning up all my courage, plunged my hand in and grabbed him by his back. He tried to fight back, but I was a vet and knew what I was doing. Holding him firmly I shouted "Ready". Clare lifted the lid, and I went to pop him into the boiling water. At this point he grabbed the sides with his pincers. Clare screamed. I screamed. I dropped Clickety Clack, who scuttled off underneath an old drying chest. We both fled outside for champagne.

By the time we returned to have another go, the boiling pan had managed to make a small cloud that hung for about a yard from the ceiling. There was a slow drip, drip, drip, from various areas, and the floor was now slippery with moisture. In fact, as far as Clickety Clack was concerned, we seemed to be creating an ideal lobster home.

We were both vets, and felt bad that we weren't being at all professional about this. Clare refilled the pot with water and, once it was boiling furiously, I hooked Clickety Clack out from under the dryer. He fought back like the devil, but I was ready for him this time. Clare lifted the lid, and I popped the poor fellow in backwards. We ran. We really didn't want to hear the scream, so whether there was one or not I don't know.

Fifteen minutes later, and chefs please don't write to say too long, we tiptoed back in. The curtain of steam was half way down the walls now. Clickety Clack was bright pink, and very dead.

We hauled him out and popped him onto the old wooden table. We sat down either side of him and stared. There were two emotions, really. Both of us felt very sad, but I also felt very ill. All the champagne and the overwhelming smell of Grimsby docks that hung in the air was making me nauseous.

We couldn't eat him. We left him there on the table and, after opening the window, left for the pubs. There we drowned our sorrows and drank to the memory of Clickety Clack who had been needlessly taken from this world.

In the morning, through the mists of our hangover, we stared at the evidence of our sin. He was there as a cold pink reminder of our cruelty. We didn't want to face him.

What should we do?

Clare though we might give him to Nora. Nora was the caretaker who looked after the cottage. She was in her 80s, and had lived in Kilbaha all her life.

We lifted Clickety Clack solemnly onto a plate and carried him round. We rang on the door, but no answer. So, writing a note, we left our offering on the steps leading up to the door.

'Thought you might like a lobster.'

Nora, even though she had lived in a fishing village all her life, had never had a lobster before. It was far too expensive.

She popped round the next day to say thank you. I feel a bit guilty about this, as it started a tradition in the village. Now, anyone who rents the cottage must pay a tax of one lobster to Nora. She, however, worships us, and still asks after that lovely honeymoon couple.

Chapter Four

I had been at The Mount Vet Group for about three and a half years when I began to realise that the time had come to move on. I had hoped to stay there and become a partner; however, things were not meant to be, so I began to look around for somewhere to go. Clare and I had been renting a lovely farmhouse just south of Malton, at Gally Gap, and had gradually been building up a menagerie. Any move would have to take the pack into consideration.

The family now included psychotic geese, chickens (no eggs), two pet sheep (Lucky and Blue), turkeys (that never made it to the Xmas table), doves, an ex race horse Andorra (still lame, despite horse boffin's attentions) and, of course, Kipper.

We Brits always favour the underdog, and I am no exception when choosing my pets. If I had to choose from a litter of guinea pigs, I would quite happily pick the smallest, daftest looking one that nobody else would have. If I had to choose a goldfish from a huge tank of them, I'd go for the one floating on its back. So when I decided I wanted a dog, I went along to the RSPCA and picked out Kipper. He came from a choice of three puppies they had. He was lame, had fleas, worms and mange, and had a twist in his neck that forced his head five inches to his left. He was such an individual looking dog I fell for him instantly. With his really long ears and his head to one side, he caught the attention of many people over the eight years we had him. On walks, fellow walkers would often enquire what breed he was. I got tired of explaining his neck twist so I told them Kipper was a 'Hungarian twisted weasel hound' and that his oddly angled neck enabled him to seek out weasels around corners. Kipper had arrived to keep Fly, Clare's whippet, company. Fly, however, never noticed he was there as she rarely climbed out from under her duvet. When she did, we all reeled because of the ever-worsening halitotic breath, but she was nearly 16 so of course had the hygiene standards of any teenager.

The icing on the cake, though, was Hilary the pig. Hilary was given to me as a Christmas present in 1993, funnily enough by David Harrison, son of Mr Harrison the pig farmer. Maybe Yorkshire farmers have a conscience, or perhaps just a sense of humour ... of sorts. We named her after my sister, for reasons that are still a mystery.

When she came into season it was a nightmare, as she could quite easily smash any fencing down as she wandered off to find a mate. Hell hath no fury like a randy pig. One year I rather pompously announced I planned to get her pregnant by artificial insemination. How hard could it really be? After all I am a vet!

I joined the Yorkshire pig breeders' association and they sent me a catalogue listing all the types of sperm we could buy. Really, they have a catalogue! It's not something like ...

Two ounces of
Landrace Boar
Size XL
£50 or 10 weeks at £5

but it does exist. Clare and I spent a hilariously childish evening reading it before deciding what sort of piglets we wanted. Once we had decided on the father, we sent off our 10 pounds and waited.

I am not sure what I expected, but a small plastic squeezy bottle with a long corkscrew catheter was not it. Certainly the postman raised an eyebrow as I signed for a sperm sample. Why it couldn't have come in a brown envelope, I don't know, and I would have preferred it to have said 'pig sperm sample' rather than just sperm.

Pigs have a unique reproduction system, and insemination necessitates winding the catheter into place in the urethra until it is locked. The plan was simple: Clare would feed Hilary whilst I wound the catheter into place. After attaching the bottle, I would up-end it to allow the sample to enter the womb.

However, all did not go quite according to plan. Having screwed the catheter into place, I went to attach the bottle only to discover it had a sealed lid. The little sign on the bottle indicated I should cut off the top with scissors, but I was stuck in a muddy pig pen, holding onto a catheter in my left hand, and about to lose my wellies. The only thing to do was to bite off the lid with my teeth. I did this in a rush and a panic, only to get a face full of pig sperm. Clare burst into laughter. If the postman had turned up with the second post at that moment I wouldn't have blamed him for reporting me to the police.

Hilary finished her food and sauntered off, leaving me wallowing in the mud trying desperately to hold onto the catheter. As each welly got sucked off, I began to accept that perhaps artificial insemination wasn't the doddle I had deemed it to be.

The following morning, cap in hand, I rang David. Later that day Henry, a rather superlative boar, arrived to do the business. Hilary went on to have two litters of piglets that raced in and out of the house through the cat flap. But all the while Hilary continued to grow and grow, to become a strapping eight-foot long sow with unusual needs. She developed a taste for eating candles and going for long walks. When we went to work, she would get bored, break out and push open our front door. Once in, she would seek out candles to nibble whilst re-arranging all the furniture or using it as scratching posts.

I still had to leave The Mount Vet Group. My first practice in Winchester offered me a partnership and I was quite tempted to go back down to Hampshire, but the traffic there was awful. Similarly, we looked at moving to a veterinary practice in Lincolnshire. However, Clare's boss, Edmund Collins, suggested that I speak to a man called Stuart Easby in Stamford Bridge. He thought Stuart was looking for somebody to take over running his small animal practice. I rang Stuart and he suggested we have lunch. So the following day I went down to Stamford Bridge and he and I went out for a Chinese lunch. It was a great success, I liked the man immediately; he had a great twinkle in his eyes and a fantastic sense of humour. Though he did have a beard! We had a riotous lunch and I knew that I had finally found a home. His wife, Pauline, was the practice manager. She was highly efficient and would spend all hours of the day and night there organising everything for the two of us.

The day I left The Mount was 10 February 1995, and I know it was that date because that was the day our first son, Jack, was born. If you ask Clare what the good things in life are, she will say castrating horses, undoing knots and dancing, although not necessarily in that order. I think she has missed something out: giving birth to our sons.

Jack was born in Malton hospital. Clare had attended maternity lessons with a midwife who had persuaded her that a water birth is the way to go. I had very little to do with the preparations. I had attended the compulsory meeting of prospective parents, where they get to watch the equivalent of a horror movie on childbirth. I think the main object of the video is to stun fathers into complete silence so that they don't interfere in any way. After that video, I decided that animals had the right idea: not to worry about it until it happened. Then at the time, if all goes well, fine; if not, call a vet. So Clare and the midwife rented a swimming pool, which the hospital kindly put up in one of their labour wards. They had never seen a water birth either, and were fascinated as well. I went to read up on the subject and discovered that early mammals, just after the dinosaurs went extinct, had given birth in the water, so maybe Clare's argument that it was natural was true. On the great day everything went 'swimmingly'. Jack popped out into this world in the middle of the night, whilst I did the crossword and drank whisky from a Thermos, having lied to the midwife saying it was coffee. We were attended by dozens of midwives and junior doctors, who all wanted to watch a water birth. Clare, who has a pretty high pain threshold, never let out a squeak, and so the medical world went away deeply impressed with the pain-relieving properties of water births. I didn't have the heart to tell them that even when Clare fell off a ladder breaking lots of ribs she never let out a sound. She leaves all that kind of whinging to me and the kids.

I remember celebrating Jack's birth in our local pub, the Jolly Farmers in Leavening, apparently demonstrating the mating habits of the ferret at four in the morning. Needless to say I cannot remember a thing about it, and am not sure I even know the mating habits of the ferret, but what a great night. I think. This is how exotic vets make their reputations, or is it break them?

I then had six weeks off work to recover from that night and get accustomed to fatherhood. Clare and I whizzed round the countryside showing anyone, including passers-by, our newborn son.

On arriving at my new place of work, well rested, I leapt straight in. The deal was that I would run the small animals whilst Stuart did the horses and cows. For legal reasons I was unable to do the veterinary work at the Zoo for two years, but I was busy enough.

After just a year of working for Stuart, he invited me to become his partner, and I accepted. Steadily the surgeries and the work grew. After a couple of years, we managed to persuade Andrew to leave The Mount and come and join us to run the surgery at Strensall.

Later there was a gap for a small animal veterinary surgery in Pocklington, so we set up a branch there. Slowly but surely we grew and grew. Six years later, Stuart decided to retire early so he could enjoy life to the full, now that his children had grown up and left home. His wife decided she was going too. I don't blame them, but I still miss their kindness and advice.

Let's just get a grim fact out of the way. Veterinary work is hard work and forces you to face a gamut of emotions every single day. From bringing a new life into the animal world, to telling a dear old lady her best friend, a canary, didn't make it through an operation. It can be tough. Vets have the highest suicide rate of any profession. A friend of mine, whilst stuck in traffic with me, once asked me why. I told him because it was so easy.

"I have enough narcotics in the back of my car to bump off you, me and everyone else in the traffic jam."

He went very quiet and never got inside my car again. Well, he asked!

So I took over from Stuart to become sole proprietor of the three Battleflatts surgeries at Pocklington, Stamford Bridge and Strensall. Had I bitten off more than I could chew, you're probably asking. Good question. I'll let you know when I've finished chewing.

Over all this time I built up a large collection of friends and clients with exotic pets, and one of these was the RSPCA. I had done a lot of work for them over the years, mainly related to wild animals, and it was for this reason that they had asked me to go on the Scarborough parrot raid where I first met Katie.

After that initial meeting with her, I heard no more for a good six months or so, so I was surprised one day when Katie rang wanting a meeting. Real Life Media Productions had been commissioned to film a series of short five-minute programmes based at the Zoo, which would then fit into a new evening programme called *Tonight* on ITV Yorkshire. So my television career was finally to begin.

Chapter Five

That initial phone call from Katie, after not hearing for so long, got me very excited. All sorts of mad ideas flooded into my mind: stardom, a record contract, trips to Hollywood to direct the movie 'Matt Brash – Zoovet In Space', perhaps even a guest spot on *Teletubbies*. However, veterinary work is a great leveller, and the next phone call I received soon brought me back to earth. Though before I tell you about that, I must say that the title exotic vet still makes me giggle to myself, as it always conjures up an image of a vet in a grass skirt, with a garland of flowers, dancing some sort of hula-hula! Anyway back to my point.

It was Mrs Jones, ringing to inquire whether I was free to come and look at her parrot, a macaw named Malcolm. Malcolm was an old friend but he and I had not always had a rosy relationship. One of the more important things to being a successful exotic vet is actually being able to catch your patient, and this was a lesson I had learnt whilst working in Beverley, when I had first met Malcolm.

While people usually bring their cat or dog to the vets under their arms, owners of wild and exotic animal have a myriad of ways of transporting their beloved creatures. I have had tortoises on leads, parrots on shoulders, snakes in handbags and enormous many-legged unrecognisable nasties in cardboard boxes.

Back then, Mrs Jones had first rung wanting me to clip Malcolm's toenails but, as she was an invalid, she needed a home visit.

"You'll understand when you see him," she told me.

Perhaps I should have taken that as an early warning sign, but I didn't. I had little experience of macaws, but I'm an optimist and asked myself how hard can it be? My boss smiled knowingly and suggested that I took a pair of gardening gloves with me, and went off to play golf chuckling to himself.

I arrived to find the sweet old lady sitting in her chair with her Zimmer frame beside her, sucking parma violet sweets and listening to the radio. The heat in the room was stifling, but that's how these old birds like it. So do their parrots.

She called, "Come in, dear."

In I went and there, at the far end of the living room, was a beautiful blue and gold macaw chewing on a picture frame. He looked up, cocked his head to one side and went back to destroying the picture. She told me she was worried because his toenails were getting a bit long and might damage her skin when he came for a cuddle. He didn't look like the cuddly sort to me.

Girding my loins, I approached Malcolm slowly with my gloves on. Malcolm dropped the picture and eyed me malevolently. As I got closer, he decided to relocate to the other end of the room. There he took to destroying the remains of her dado rail. Half an hour later I had been sufficiently exercised but Malcolm was beginning to really enjoy this game. The intense heat of the room was getting to me by then, and I was beginning to really hate this parrot.

Mrs Jones piped up and enquired, "How are you getting on?"

"Fine," I said, gasping air into my lungs, "just fine."

"He's a good natured little chap isn't he," she said, and I realised that perhaps her eyesight was not all it could be.

I finally managed to corner him. This was when I learnt my first big lesson about parrots, or at least about macaws: with them, attack is the best form of defence.

As I grabbed hold of him with my heavy duty gardening-gloved hands, he instantly sank his beak straight through the gloves, straight into my flesh. The pain was excruciating, but I didn't yell as that would have been unprofessional.

"He's playful isn't he," said Mrs Jones.

A few curt and coarse answers sprang to mind, but I made them stay there. Malcolm's legs grabbed hold of my other arm in a vice-like grip. Oh yes, he did need his nails cutting. I winced. I was stuck; a true Catch 22 situation. I had him in a vet lock and he had me in a parrot handcuff. What to do next? Blood was beginning to drip off my arm onto the floor. My blood!

Mrs Jones was beginning to realise what was going on.

"Is he alright, dear?" asked the old lady, concerned. "I am sure I can see some blood, you haven't hurt him, have you?"

I assured her through gritted teeth that he was fine, and no thank you I wouldn't like another parma violet. A plaster would have been nice! I realised that I had to let go of his body with my left hand to stand any chance of either escape or progress. However, at this point he took the matter into his own claws. He let go with his beak. This allowed him to get a better grip on my right arm with his claws, and he then reached forwards and took a large bite out of my now totally exposed open hand.

It took me another quarter of an hour to gently ply each toenail off my arm, at which point I was able to clip it slightly before replacing it back in the hole it had dug. After about an hour I had finally managed to clip most of the toenails and the blood was flowing freely down my arm.

"I've finished," I said, adding under my breath, "I'm just not sure he's finished with me."

However, Malcolm had had enough, and when I walked towards his perch he hopped gaily back onto it and returned to chewing holes in the curtains, as if nothing had ever happened.

"You're quite sure he's alright?" came the call from the corner, "He's very sensitive."

"Oh yes," I replied, wrapping my shirt sleeves tightly round my arms to slow the bleeding a bit, "he's fine."

"Well thank you so much my dear. Cheerio," she responded, as I fled to my car.

The wounds healed, but I did learn two big lessons. Firstly, you have to catch your patient, secondly you have to restrain them safely once you've got them. This is not always as easy as it sounds. I am not saying we always get it right, and those wounds certainly haven't been the last I've ever received from an animal. But the true secret lies in knowing what they are going to do next, because then you can be ready for them. Even when they decide to have a go at you, you've had it if you show them any sign of fear.

It was also the last time I ever used a glove to handle a parrot. A towel is a better tool than gloves because the parrot cannot work out exactly where your fingers then are. So much less painful. In fact, nowadays I give towel lessons to all the parrot owners I come across, so that the birds are used to being caught.

On this particular day, years later, when she rang wanting a visit, I knew exactly what to do; I had catching Malcolm down to a tee. On arrival, I had a peanut or two ready in my pocket as a treat. A large towel thrown swiftly over him to subdue him, and the toenails were easily done. Malcolm, however, views me very much as a second-rate vet because I am no longer willing to spend time playing parrot handcuffs. On this occasion, he still managed to dig one of his toes well into the palm of my hand, just as a little reminder of who was boss.

The following week Katie came over, and I must have seemed like a little kid on Christmas morning as I rattled off all the ideas I had and where I thought the show would go. She explained, as delicately as possible, that she didn't think I was ever going to become the new David Attenborough.

She told me they wanted to film a series of short stories to be fitted into the *Tonight* programme on ITV. They were to be 'feel-good factor' programmes, with nice endings and jolly music, all in a five-minute, digestible nutshell. Yuk, I gagged. I was just to act as a vet and not as a presenter at all. I was very unsure; it all sounded very saccharine. But Katie talked me round and, with Clare reminding me that one of my college friends who worked for the BBC had spent the first two years of his TV career dressed either as a chicken or a giraffe, I was persuaded.

The next thing to do was to get the Zoo's agreement. I feel very strongly that when I am at the Zoo I am there as their vet and will give them 100%; any filming could not interfere with that. Again Katie was very persuasive, convincing both myself and the Zoo management that this would continue to be the case. With everything agreed, the following month we started filming the first series of *Zoo Vet*.

Chapter Six

Katie would arrive at the surgery early in the morning, and she and I would travel up to the Zoo together, planning features and plotting filming schedules. Katie would just follow me around the Zoo, filming hours and hours of material that could be edited down into interesting vignettes. On some occasions there would be nothing to do, while at other times we would be run off our feet. The only consideration I had to make to the camera was to ensure that I spoke clearly and slowly, explaining what was the problem, the solution and how I was to go about it. Katie had an infectious giggle and an easy manner that made me feel relaxed. To get me used to the camera's presence, she would prompt me with questions when I wasn't explaining myself. She would tell me I'd gone quiet and that the thoughts that were leaping to mind should be made to leap a tad higher and actually come out of my mouth. I soon learned that, unless I kept explaining what I was doing, people might think they were watching some Mr Bean-type silent comedy set in a zoo.

Katie is a born photographer and great with animals too, always knowing exactly where to stand when we were working. I feel that it was the combination of our rapport, the amazing animals and our individual skills that led to the success of *Zoo Vet*.

As I only ever went to Flamingo Land every other Wednesday, it took a long time for them to get enough material for their little five-minute episodes. But Katie was patient and seemed to be able to make stories out of the most mundane and routine cases, as they seemed to me in any case.

However, not everything always went totally to plan. One of the very first things we filmed was the South American condors. Trying to mimic the conditions in the wild where they live is something we strive to achieve at the Zoo. So when the opportunity arose to expand the size of their cage, the zookeepers grasped at it. The condors have lived there for a long time. The male condor is probably the oldest inhabitant of the Zoo, being nearly 55 years old now. He had lived with his wife for nearly 25 years. Every year, they would lay an egg but, sadly, she would always clumsily break it. We had tried everything under the sun to stop this, making different types and shapes of nest boxes. Usually they nested on the ground, a different corner each year. When we built a box off the ground, she was thrilled, and took to using it immediately. However, that year she rolled the egg out and it broke. So next we built a little lip on the inside of the nest box; this stopped her rolling the egg out, and so she took to cracking it instead.

More space was available, and so their enclosure size was doubled. This had disastrous and unpredicted consequences. Very quickly, it became apparent that he was deeply insecure, almost agoraphobic, and he became aggressive towards his wife. He would attack her, damaging her badly on her neck with his beak. We quickly separated them. As soon as we put them back together, he would start attacking her again. Obviously, something more dramatic was going to have to be done. What struck me as being logical was to try and blunt the instrument of his torture, i.e. his beak. He wasn't damaging her in any way with his toes, only with his beak. I felt that if I could blunt his beak for a period of time whilst he rebuilt his self-confidence, then they might settle back into a normal routine.

To this end, we planned to catch him, anaesthetise him and then build a prosthesis on the end of his beak, made out of a resin that we normally use for creating artificial hooves on cattle's feet when they go lame.

Catching the vulture was the first task and, although I had been dreading this, remembering what Malcolm had achieved, in fact he was quite a softy. He sat in a corner staring at us, puffing himself up as large as he could and spreading his wings. But when we didn't run away, a look of panic crossed his face and he just lay there. However, his defence mechanisms were not over yet. As we threw a large towel over him, and then grabbed his feet, he immediately vomited. Many of the vulture family do this when stressed. A charming habit, really. Their regurgitated food is one of the most revolting and smelliest mixtures I have ever been covered in. Katie, filming religiously, giggled.

Having caught him, we carried him to the operating theatre at the Zoo and anaesthetised him. This was a simple procedure, involving placing a modified face mask over his head, and gassing him with Isoflorane. This extremely safe, gaseous anaesthetic is a 'god-send' to bird vets. The birds tolerate the smell, and fall asleep quickly and easily. When you turn the gas off they wake up just as quickly. With him safely asleep, I set to, cutting a number of grooves in his upper beak to which I could then attach the resin. It sets quickly, and within five minutes it was rock hard and I was delighted. I turned to the camera proudly to show off my handiwork. Filming was going to be fun. We carried him back to his enclosure and he soon woke up. Katie carefully filmed his recovery, and minutes later he stood up. He carefully eyed us and then, with a casual flick of his head, the prosthesis flew off his beak and landed some 10 feet away. I was back to square one. Katie giggled; I muttered. Perhaps filming wasn't going to be so much fun.

Plan B was put into action two weeks later. This involved drilling a steel pin through his upper beak to keep the resin in place. We re-caught him, got vomited on again, and took him back to the operating theatre. Again under general anaesthetic, I drilled a steel pin straight through his upper beak and then moulded the resin putty into place on top of this. On recovery this worked well and, although he shook his head, it did not fall off.

We left the lumpy prosthesis in place for about six weeks. He did his best to attack and maul his wife, but to no avail. However hard he tried to bite and rip her skin, all that happened was the round hard ball would run along the top of her skin. When we took the prosthesis off, after six weeks, the two of them had calmed down and they have lived happily together ever since. She, however, continues to break her eggs! All was well in the end, but with filming Katie was going to get me warts and all.

Although my routine visits were on a Wednesday, whenever we had more complicated procedures to carry out I would often block out at least a day or two. One such example was the problem of the flamingos.

In the centre of Flamingo Land Zoo there is a large lake surrounded by drooping willow trees, with a small island in the centre. It is colonised by large numbers of wild waterfowl, particularly itinerant barnacle and Canada geese, but it is really home to 100 flamingos. Some creatures we are desperate to breed, and flamingos are one of them. These chaps had been a headache for me since my early days at the Zoo. They wouldn't get on with it, and we couldn't work out why. They used to breed regularly, often producing up to about 10 young per year, when they were looked after by a laid-back keeper, Sean. He used to mother them and hand feed them on bits of bread and leftover scraps from the nearby cafe. This was stopped because of feeding regulations, and at the same time they stopped breeding. As the years went by, they continually failed to reproduce and ever more wild theories were put forward to explain the lack of progeny. The keepers tried everything. Their diet was switched to expensive flamingo breeding pellets, but this had no effect. Large amounts of mud were supplied for them to build their tall conical nests; nothing. They tried to build their nests, but that year the early summer was particularly wet and muddy, and the nests were just washed away. So we built them concrete nests, to give them a head start. These were then covered in mud for them, so they would have less work to do; nothing. An artificial stream that flowed through this concrete jungle was created, so they would already have a source of the correct type of mud; nothing. It was all to no avail. They would begin nesting, but almost invariably it seemed something would happen and they would give up. Perhaps it was just the rotten Yorkshire weather.

One spring another possible reason for their lack of breeding aroused suspicion. We found a dead flamingo with nasty bite marks in its neck. A post mortem showed the death had resulted from a bite from a small weasel or stoat-like creature. Mink were known to be living on the river and we wondered if they were to blame. So the flamingos were housed inside each night and we set traps and, sure enough, within a week we caught a mink. Indeed, we continued to catch them all that year. We were beginning to think we'd cracked the problem. But no, the flamingos still failed to breed. This was now becoming a bit of a passion of mine, or I was at least becoming obsessed.

I turned my attentions to the birds themselves. The next logical move was to understand exactly what we had in terms of flamingos. Were they all male or all female? Perhaps that was the problem. The decision was taken to anaesthetise all the flamingos, check them all over and surgically sex them. Although the sex of some birds can be determined by looking at them from the outside, such as with pheasants, flamingos fundamentally look the same. There is a slight difference between males and females, but there is such an overlap you cannot be entirely accurate. All birds have internal ovaries or testes in the top of the abdomen so, by making a small hole in the left-hand side of the abdomen, I could insert my endoscope and view the gonads or lady bits.

There were 99 of them, made up of Chilean, Cuban and greater flamingos, and Katie was to film the whole proceedings.

Now, the flamingo is as gentle as it looks and very fragile. Catching one is all the more difficult because they are nervous birds and their spindly legs have a tendency to break. They are the Julian Clarys of the animal world. One thing was for sure, if we were to do this, it would have to be done on a day when the Zoo was closed to the public, so that there would be minimum disturbance, and the operation would have to be very smooth.

A large corral was prepared. This involved building scaffolding that was padded with plastic all around its 10-foot high sides. It was placed between the flamingoes lake and their night quarters, so that they walked through it on a daily basis and began to get used to it. Their keeper, Jackie, who they trusted, would herd them through the corral every evening as she put them to bed, and in the morning they walked out through it to get to their lake.

Finally the day for our work came. The birds were released from their overnight shelter, and they came out calmly into the corral. Jackie was placed inside, and she caught them one by one. Having caught a flamingo, she would pass it out to one of the other keepers. They would grip it under their arm and bring it into the shed, where I was waiting to do the anaesthetising and surgical sexing. A tight hold had to be kept on those long spindly legs for fear they would break.

I had brought Diana with me from the practice to act as anaesthetist, and at nine o'clock in the morning we were off. Katie was filming, and by lunchtime we were whizzing along, having done nearly 40 birds. However, after lunch, as we got more and more tired, it began to get slower and we certainly began to become somewhat 'flamingo happy'. By the end of the day, we had successfully anaesthetised and surgically sexed all 99 flamingos, finishing at seven thirty in the evening.

I found there to be ... an exactly even split.

So why weren't they at it like rabbits? The rabbits were!

Each flamingo had had a yellow plastic ring put on either its right or its left leg. Females had the ring on their left leg, and males had the ring on their right. Each ring had a three-letter code, such as *x, y, z,* or *a, b, c,* so that we could tell which bird was which in future. I'd taken blood samples from every fifth flamingo to see how healthy they were overall, so also had a pile of blood samples. Maybe these would give us the answer. One thing for sure, we were all shattered.

The bloods were sent off and, after analysis, we discovered that all the birds were leukaemic; they had hardly any white blood cells. I could only put this down to the birds being faced with an overwhelming chronic infection. Yet they all looked OK. The lack of white blood cells would certainly have a knock-on effect in terms of breeding. If the problem was not diet or sex ratio, then it had to be the environment. The trees were cut back to give them more daylight. I was even tempted to stick a telly in their enclosure and show them blue movies: heck, I'd tried everything else.

I turned my attention to looking at the lake. The lake, of course, had had all these wild Canada and barnacle geese for many years, as well as the flamingos, and really was probably rather smelly, although it looked OK from the outside. Anyway, the lake in Africa where they all congregate is far more toxic looking; but we decided that the lake had to be drained. More than 500 tons of sludge were removed from the lake, and then it was refilled. At the same time, we used the occasion to heighten the perimeter fence; although we had caught mink, we also suspected that foxes might come through at night and, having lost birds to foxes, I wanted to ensure that foxes were not going to harass the birds at the time of nesting.

It took time, but all our modifications and hard work paid off. After 10 years of trying, in 2006 they finally laid an egg. In fact they laid nearly 20, and they managed to raise 12 chicks. Success, at last. Maybe the flamingos just decided it was time to settle down with a family. It happens to us all.

It was around now that Clare and I decided that the time had really come for us to grow up, leave our lovely rented farmhouse at Gally Gap and own our house. We had been renting the old farmhouse for four years, and had had a lovely time. But, as Clare's father put it, we were really just camping. The house was 200 years old; the cracks in the frames of the old sash windows were so wide that the wind use to whistle through the house at such a pace it could make the carpet rise up off the floor. I had finally managed to get Clare interested in growing vegetables, and even she had succumbed to the glories of growing one's own purple-sprouting broccoli. Jack had been born whilst we were there, and so too had our second son, Charlie, one year later.

We have always had spring babies; it is so much nicer to have the summer off. I was out playing bridge when Clare went into labour with Charlie. She had been spending her time usefully lusting after George Clooney on ER. So it was her own fault really.

Giving birth in humans seems to me to be a long and arduous process, but fortunately there was a good movie on to pass the time. Charlie, like Jack, was born in the middle of the night and looked, to me, identical to his brother. Everyone else seemed to notice that he had his grandmother's eyes, or his father's head. This worried me, as it all looked rather blotchy and crumpled to me.

With our expanding family, the time had indeed come to move. So the search for a new home began.

Chapter Seven

Wherever we were going, it had to be spacious and have as large a garden as possible, so that Clare could continue to keep a horse. The difficulty was that, as we are both vets, it also needed to be within spitting distance of both of our places of work, and this was never going to be easy. Plus there were 'night call outs' to consider. We needed to be in close proximity to our clients. Night calls are a pain, but they're an excellent way to stay off the alcohol. Otherwise getting there at two in the morning to see an emergency becomes a possible lawsuit.

Finally we found what looked to us to be the perfect place: Brook Cottage, an early 18th century pair of cottages that had been knocked together in the 1960s. It had belonged to a client of mine who had sadly passed away. His three sons lived out of the region and were selling it, but there had been no interest in the property. The reason being that on both sides of the cottage people were planning to build houses. This didn't bother us too much. There was a large garden and small paddock opposite so all of our criteria were met and we moved in.

The cottage was placed in the middle of the vibrant village of Leavening. There was a small local primary school that was short of numbers, so they were delighted that we were moving to the village. So delighted, in fact, that they enrolled poor Jack at the age of three and half so that they could get their numbers up.

There was just one cloud on our horizon, however. There was really no practical way that Hilary the pig was going to be able to stay with us. She was now of an enormous size and, although she did agree to pretend to stay behind her electric fencing, this was just a sham. Quite honestly, a wandering one-ton pig in a small village would no doubt cost us a fortune in damages, especially as she had by now discovered greenhouses. God knows what the terrified kids at the primary school would make of her. She'd probably put them off bacon for life.

David agreed to have her back. This really was one of the saddest moments we have had, and both Clare and I were devastated to say goodbye to her. Still, onward and upward.

The move went easily, as we had few possessions and they fitted into a horse lorry in two loads. Plus, we were only moving two miles up the road. The rest of the pets took a bit longer to relocate, but they came round to the idea in the end. We moved and started to unpack.

Excitement was never far round the corner, and soon we were back at the Zoo. This time to move a crocodile. The old croc had been on the surplus list for ages. All zoos have lists of surplus animals. This doesn't mean that they are going to get rid of an animal to just anyone; it is a private list of things that they think they would like to be rid of. They have another one of animals they would like to acquire. It is a good system, as it means that if a zoo is looking for a new giraffe, it knows where to go.

The crocodile had been on his own for a while, and had begun to outgrow his enclosure, so a new home was being sought. Although I was keen for him to go, I wasn't looking forward to the move itself.

He had been there so long, without any health problems of any kind, that I wondered whether he was actually still alive. In fact, I had once suggested to the Zoo that they could get a bunch of plastic reptiles and stick them in the cages and most people would never know the difference. But I suppose that's not the point.

Finally a new home was found for him. All we had to do was to get him there. This wasn't going to be easy.

Years before, the Zoo had once had a keeper, John, who was an expert on crocodiles. The last time we had moved the crocodile, John had been there on hand to help. As at that stage I had never looked at the crocodile, I had taken the opportunity to give him a health check over. John assured me that catching crocs was easy. They have immense power in their jaws to close them, he told me, but very little power to actually open them again. Once one has their jaws closed, you can easily keep them shut with just your hands. The tricky bit is to get them to that point, and still have your own hands. This, John assured me, was also easy. All you have to do is tap them on the nose. Apparently, if you tap them on the top of the nose, they get so cross they will lift their heads up to bite you. At this point all you have to do is pop your thumbs under their chins and push upwards. Eventually, as you push upwards, their mouths will shut and you can put your fingers over their snout and you've got them. Only thing is, you have to watch out for their tails at the same time, he said. Rather him than me, I remember thinking, glad that he was there.

I was as confident in my ability as John seemed to be, and could remember well having to stitch up one of his snakes. It had been a 14-foot long python that had had a lover's quarrel with its mate and come off worse. It had a foot-long gash down its neck and needed stitches. Snakes come under the category of really tricky anaesthetics. If you get the dose wrong, they can be asleep for days, so John had said that he would hold it whilst I stitched it up. He added that, if it got pissed off and wrapped itself round one of us, not to cut its head off, as it was too valuable. Pythons are, of course, constrictors, and get their prey by squeezing the life, or at least the breath, out of them. If the snake wrapped itself round one of us, then we were to wait until it had finished, then unwind it. I had stared at the snake incredulously; it had to weigh more than 10 stone. I asked Andrew, infinitely fitter and stronger than I, to help! Still, stitching it up had gone without incident. Every time the snake was beginning to look cross, we would shove its writhing coils back in its large wicker basket. Sitting on the lid, we would have another coffee whilst it calmed down. Despite local anaesthetic, it was not enjoying being put back together. It had taken more than 200 stitches and, of course, the cameras had been nowhere in sight to catch the fun.

Katie was, however, going to be there for when we moved the croc. John sadly wasn't. However, Dene was a good reptile man and, as the keeper in charge of the reptile house, he knew what he was doing. Both of us agreed we would not employ John's technique, much to Katie's disgust. I had heard on the grapevine that, since John had left, he had lost a few fingers inside a croc, so maybe his method didn't always work!

The principal we would employ was still much the same. We would have to tape up the croc's nose, so that it couldn't bite us, whilst still watching out for its tail.

We reasoned that if we could get a broom under his chin, then push up and backwards, this would do the same thing. I could then slip some sticky tape over his nose, and the rest would be easy. The croc thought differently. The first broom was bitten clean in half, and the second, made of metal, he just bent.

The added complication was that we were filming, and I was worried that Katie might get in the way and be hurt. Or, far more importantly, might get in our way, and we would get hurt. So we sent Katie out of the room. It was bad enough having to look after ourselves, without having to worry about her.

Plan B in this case was to push his head downwards, so that he couldn't open his mouth at all. This worked rather better, and finally we managed to get some tape over his nose. Now at least he wasn't going to bite us. It was an easy job then to get hold of the legs and tie these over his back. This restrains crocodiles effectively, without causing them any pain. They have immensely powerful muscles, and we didn't want him using his limbs to push us or himself around. Finally, with him trussed up, we all breathed a sigh of relief.

But this was only step one. We still had to get him out of the enclosure and then into his transport crate.

The first part of this was achieved relatively easily; we tied all 10 feet of him onto a ladder. A plank would have done just as well, but a ladder was lighter.

Once we had got him outside, we put him down and stopped for a breather. He wasn't light and we still had to work out how we were going to get him into the crate. A crate for transporting a croc is exactly what you would expect. A long, three-foot tall, three-foot wide, box. When I say long; it was about 15 foot long, giving him enough space to move up and down a bit, but not too much space that he might hurt himself in transport.

But how to get him into the box? This was not something that could be done with him tied up, as we could never safely get the sticky tape off his nose in the box. He would have to be freed whilst out of the box and then coerced in. This sounded simple enough. With Katie loving every minute of it, we built a wall of wood either side of him, supported by an army of people. Again, being expendable, I went in to remove the tape off his snout. This was easy; unfortunately, as soon as I had done this, he turned round and started to move towards me. Perhaps he had been talking to Nelson the chimp.

Certainly we had not fully informed him of our plans and he had other ideas. He set off towards the lorry that was there to transport him. If he got under that, then we would be in real trouble. Panicking slightly, I sent one person to move the lorry, whilst the rest of us tried to steer 10 foot of cross croc in the direction we needed him to go in. Where was John, or even Steve Irwin, when we needed him: finally, we managed to get him back facing the right way. Now all we needed him to do was to walk forwards into the crate. But he obstinately refused to go. I certainly wasn't going to go in there Crocodile Dundee-style to drag him in, and none of the others were keen. We needed yet another plan B.

Eventually, after a stalemate of 15 minutes or so, someone came up with the idea of dragging him by looping a rope over his front legs. We threw a rope down his crate to the other end, then looped one end over each of his front legs. We could now slowly but surely drag him in. After he had gone a couple of yards he conceded and walked the rest of the way himself. He was safely loaded and on his way to a new home. In all our dealings with the animals at the Zoo, success is ultimately measured by no-one being hurt and the animal being OK. Our job done, and Katie happy with her filming, I returned to the unpacking at home. Life was never dull.

Zoo Vet was always filmed in this way, with much humour. Katie was so relaxed, and always willing to advise, in a terribly polite manner, how I could do things better.

I loved filming with her; it was all so easy and straight forward. This was how filming television shows was meant to be, I thought. No great effort on my part, just good fun.

From the outset of *Zoo Vet*, I had always thought it would be a 'flash in the pan' kind of thing, and had been amazed when we got a second series. Whilst filming that, I felt sure there wouldn't be any more and tried to enjoy every single second of it.

The programme was airing on the *Tonight* programme, in short, sharp jolly clips of five minutes long. Clare and the boys would patiently sit waiting to see Dad on the telly. Jack and Charlie would get very excited. When they were very young, they once sat watching it as I sat in the neighbouring room working. They could not for the life of them work out how I could manage to be both on the TV and next door at the same time. Clare kept calling me in to come and explain what was going on, but I couldn't. I am afraid at this point I have an admission to make. I have never watched *Zoo Vet*, or *Zoo Vet At Large*, or any of the telly programmes I have made. I saw one once, and winced horribly. Was I really getting that bald and middle aged? And did my voice really sound that bad? It is a bit like listening to yourself on the answer phone. No, I love doing TV; it's just watching it back that I don't like. I think I shall save watching them for my retirement, then I can bore my grandchildren one day. Unfortunately, the videos keep getting mouldy, so my plan may not work!

Chapter Eight

The move to Brook Cottage was completed at the same time as we finished filming that year's *Zoo Vet*. I was looking forward to settling in, getting organised and creating a new veg patch. The sheep, Lucky and Blue, had settled in quickly in our small paddock opposite. Or at least so we thought.

They quickly became bored with their new paddock, which wasn't anywhere near the size of the area they had to play in at Gally Gap Farm. Brook Cottage is in the middle of the village, and the sheep used the small dirt track leading into it to explore and to see who else they could make friends with.

We had only one neighbour, a scientist. To be precise, he was a botanist, as we later found out, but on our first meeting there wasn't the chance for social pleasantries, not even knocking on his door to ask to borrow a cup of sugar. The first we saw of him he was haring down the lane fussing and screaming about some wild animals that were about to destroy his life's work! Apparently Lucky and Blue had gone to visit him and discovered his back garden to be the sheep equivalent of a free swanky take-away, featuring in particular a so-far untasted delicacy, heather. They thought it was wonderful. Unfortunately, the heather in question was part of his life time's experiment and, if we weren't quick enough, his work would be put back by 10 years.

The girls were quickly caught and returned to their paddock before they could do too much damage. He was very nice about the whole affair. Me, I was just extremely relieved we hadn't brought Hilary with us.

There was an old wood at the end of the garden containing very unfestive-looking Christmas trees. Most were nearly dead; indeed a good few had given up the ghost and fallen over.

When we had originally gone to look at the house we hadn't realised, and neither had the estate agent, that the wood went with the house. As you can imagine, it was a more than pleasant surprise when we discovered it was ours. I owned a wood! I felt like gentry.

I removed half the trees to make way for our new veg plot. Some I simply had to leave alone, as there was a pair of tawny owls nesting in them and I didn't want to disturb them.

Peggy, who cleaned for us on a Thursday, one day announced that the newly cleared site was perfect for bees. I was slightly taken aback at the time, as we had actually been talking about flies, and we'd never even considered adding bees to our menagerie. It turned out Peggy had been married to a professional beekeeper for a long time and was quite an expert on the matter herself. She held me spellbound with her knowledge, and really got me thinking that a chap who actually owns a wood should really have some bees to go with it.

Coincidentally, I had a call the next day to go to a client's house whose dog had been badly stung by the bees she kept. Her dog, by an amazing stroke of bad luck, turned out to be allergic to bee stings and needed some fairly urgent treatment. We managed to save the dog easily, and over coffee afterwards

I quizzed my client about the bees. Where she had got them from, how much looking after they really needed, that sort of thing. During the conversation it became apparent that she was considering getting rid of them, and asked if I would be at all interested in taking them off her hands.

If I wanted them, it would have to be soon as they were just beginning to wake up, it being spring. This seemed like fate and, without giving it any more unnecessary rational thought, I agreed.

I rang Clare and she, being her usual supportive self, said what a great idea (perhaps I should have read her mind better). So the following day, I hitched up our small two-wheeled trailer, and drove the five miles to collect my first-ever beehive. Once there, we stoppered all the holes and tied the beehive closed with strong rope. Between the two of us, we managed to load the bees onto the back of the trailer. I drove slowly and tentatively home, holding my breath each time I went over the slightest bump. On the way, I became aware of an ever-growing, incensed hum. It was the bees, who were obviously not enjoying their move. They sounded confused and grumpy, like anyone woken early from a long slumber. And who were these sleepy-eyed little bullets of insectoid wonder going to take their mood out on? The first person they came across. Me! My second thoughts kicked in around this point.

Once home, I rushed to tell Clare that our bees had arrived and wondered if she would mind helping to move them up to their new home at the top of the garden. I then added, under my breath, that they were awake and a bit ratty too. Jack and Charlie were eager to help but, as there was only one beekeeping facemask, we thought it wise that they stayed indoors for this part of the operation. We also only had one bee suit, and Clare pointed out that if I wanted her help, she wanted the suit and the hat (which I thought was a tad cowardly, but there you go). For my protection, Clare kindly leant me a scarf.

It was a bit nerve-racking, this beekeeping lark. Heck, I had only had the idea on the Thursday and now here we were with our first beehive on the Saturday. Not entirely responsible, but Peggy was going to give us a hand. Plus, you can't look a gift bee in the mouth.

To carry the bees up to their new home, we had tied the beehive closed with rope that had a loop running up above it. Through this loop we passed a long pole, the idea being that we would carry the beehive slung between us. We didn't, however, make concessions for the age of the rickety looking beehive, nor its weight. This was where my third thoughts set in.

We managed to lift it out of the trailer, but were only able to make a few paces before we had to stop for a rest. Each time we picked the hive up, another couple of angry bees came shooting out of an ever-growing crack. They would mill around the swaying hive and then move off to investigate the cause of all the commotion: us! This tended to put both Clare and me off our stride, so we would have to put the hive down again.

Eventually, we carefully placed the bees in their new home at the top of the garden, adjacent to my newly created veg patch, and ran like buggery into the house, slamming the doors behind us. Only whisky could calm our nerves now.

The following Thursday found me excitedly waiting for Peggy's routine visit to muck us out. I couldn't wait to show off the bees, thinking she'd be incredibly impressed. I felt sure I was now an accomplished apiculturist, having spent all week reading up on the subject. I took her hand and led her up the garden path. When she saw what we'd done, her excited smile dropped and she suggested that really I was leading her up the garden path. The hive was in totally the wrong place; it needed to be in a much larger open space and should never, ever face north. I felt somewhat deflated. I had a lot to learn.

We set about relocating the hive. Peggy, of course, had all the right kit, and what she didn't have she quickly dispatched me to get. The bees remained calm and peaceful throughout this second move, as Peggy kept talking to them all the while. She introduced herself, and me, and told them exactly what she was doing for them. It worked! I didn't hear one disenchanted hum from any of them. The bees were placed on a carefully constructed plinth, then had to be fenced off as the dopey sheep were eager to taste this new thing called honey.

I was banned from looking in on the bees too early, and so had to wait a month before we prised the lid open. What confronted me was a messy vision of ancient honeycomb crawling in bees, straight out of a nightmare. What Peggy saw was a potential bee utopia that needed a complete overhaul. Pretty soon, with Peggy's expert guidance, my one beehive become two. Peggy told me I needed a new queen. Where on earth do you get a queen bee from, you're probably asking, as did I. Pretty easy really, you can send off for them through the post. (Had they really invented bee-mail?) A queen set me back 100 pounds, but it was worth every penny. It all went fantastically until Peggy, sadly, had to move away from the area. The bees lost their favourite human and were left with 'that idiot bloke' to look after them. I obviously didn't speak the correct language, or at least in the correct tone, because they just wouldn't do a thing I asked them to.

They decided to swarm over to my neighbour's garden. I spent several hours perched up a ladder trying to persuade them to come back, but they would have none of it. Beekeeping was obviously not for me, but I had learnt a lot and was forever grateful for the insect insights that had been shown to me. Clare pointed out that the three pots of honey we had produced were perhaps worthy of Harrod's prices.

Chapter Nine

My vet friends from college had heard about my antics in TV work, and thought it hilarious. When one of my oldest friends, John, a vet based just outside Manchester, was approached by the BBC to take part in a TV show with Trude Mostue, he declined, but told them he knew of a vet-turned media whore who would fit the bill perfectly.

The BBC were making a new show, based at the wonderful zoo at Chester, called *Vets To The Rescue*. It was to be fronted by the famous Norwegian vet, Trude Mostue. The series was due to be aired at lunchtime and was based loosely on the idea of *Antiques Roadshow* meets *Gardeners' Question Time*. Clients, who had been found at local vet surgeries, were to come with their pet to the show to be treated.

They rang to see if I would be interested in taking part. I was definitely interested, but I was worried because the title of the show made it sound like a camp superhero-type show. What if they wanted us to wear skin-tight lycra with red capes and masks and things. Naive of me, yes, but hey, this is television! And vet work is quite mundane for the better part; they'd have to jazz it up somehow. I knew for sure that I couldn't dress like a superhero, I'd look like Superman's dad!

They came over to check me out and carry out a screen test. By the time they arrived, I had finished surgery and the only thing left they could film was me clipping a greyhound's toenails. The producer was keen to hear my voice on tape, and kept prompting me to ask more and more questions about the dog. However, I knew the owner well and this was a coursing greyhound, something she was understandably nervous about in front of the cameras.

After that initial meeting, silence fell for several months and I assumed I had missed my chance of a bigger TV exposure. Then, out of the blue, they asked me to go for another screen test in Cheltenham. With trepidation, I caught a train to Cheltenham and turned up at the interview with my stomach held firmly in. Once there I began to relax, ever so slightly. I was being silly. This was the BBC for goodness sake. World-renowned consummate professionals who took their work seriously. There were three of us there for a screen test. One was so short he was nearly a dwarf, and wore shorts and Jesus sandals. The other was immensely tall with thick glasses that made his eyes appear to bulge. Very unphotogenic, the pair of them, I unfairly thought.

I think it was nerves that was making me so bitchy, but I began to feel that, compared with the others, I might look OK in my lycra suit. After a long wait, Trude arrived to check us over and we were taken, one by one, for our screen tests. We had to pretend to be examining a dog's ear for a suspected ear infection. The dog, needless to say, thought the whole thing ridiculous and was becoming increasingly more fractious. We had been filming for half an hour when a halt was called. There was a technical fault. Trude enquired what the problem was. Apparently the BBC, the aforementioned 'world-renowned consummate professionals who took their work seriously' had forgotten to put any film in their camera. Not only that, they had even forgotten to bring any film with them. A man was duly dispatched to Bristol to go and find some. I just hoped he remembered to come back. Two hours later he did, and the screen test began again. My fears of lycra abounded, as I sat in the train on my return from Cheltenham later that evening.

Much to my surprise, I got the job. I was going to work alongside Trude! I reckoned I was to be the male blond bimbo! No lycra was to be involved, fortunately. In each episode, Trude and I were there as the resident vets, whilst we had two colleagues along to make up the numbers. There was also a fifth vet, Noel Walker, who was Chester Zoo's vet and would do his bits from that very location. Occasionally the filming would pan over to him to see what he was doing and I got really jealous because he *always* had something very, very interesting on the go. Lucky swine.

Filming began in May, and we filmed every weekend over that summer. In some ways it was quite a strain to work all week, then drive over to Chester on the Friday evening and film all weekend. But the gods were shining on us and it was one of those, long, hot glorious summers, which actually made it all seem effortless. I'd arrive on set first thing in the morning and immediately aim for the make-up caravan. I would spend a happy half hour being pampered and pawed, and I loved it. My hair would be combed and styled with all sorts of sprays, gels and whatnots. Make-up was applied, making the years fall away. Clare says they must have got a plasterer in to hide my crow's feet and laughter lines. They always managed it, though, and 30 minutes later I was 'ready'. I can now quite understand why some women spend so long getting ready, it's fun! The rest of the day was spent reading good books and snoozing gently in the sunshine.

Our third son, Alfie, had recently been born, paddling his way into the world, and so sleep at home was even less than usual. I loved it, it was all so surreal. Like being involved in a gigantic play!

When required, the runners (the film unit's gophers) would come and find me, to tell me when I would be needed and where to go. They supplied me with tea and coffee too.

Three 'surgeries' had been set up in tents just adjacent to the zoo. Each client consultation was meant to be only approximately two minutes long. Two minutes! This was remarkably challenging in its own right, as it often takes nearly that amount of time just to take the temperature of an animal. In my opinion, this is where the show fell down. Trying to make a diagnosis in such a short period of time and discussing difficult issues was almost impossible. Everyone was herded round like cattle, with the audience being bussed in from the local area; it all felt very staged, and vets are not actors.

On other occasions, we were asked by the producers if we would answer some short questions. The idea being that, as we were sitting idly in between takes, a passing member of the public could benefit from our alleged encyclopaedic knowledge of, erm, oh what are they called again? Animals, that's it!

We would be proffered a list of half a dozen questions, from which we could choose two or three that we felt we would like to answer. The producers were always particularly careful about the language we used, as the show was to go out to a lunchtime audience, so when someone said would I mind answering a question from a member of the public about how one goes about getting a ram 'steamed up' ready for 'tupping' I was most perplexed. Steamed up means, basically, to be made randy, or ready for sex, and tupping means the act of sex. Oh well, I thought, this is nature, fair enough. "Of course I will," I replied. The BBC were very keen, because it was about sheep, but it then occurred to me perhaps they hadn't fully understood the question. But at least they understood what a ram was.

The time came for me to answer the actual question. A lady walked up dragging a rather reluctant Hebridian ram on a lead. She sat down next to me on the stage, surrounded by a crowd who were waiting eagerly for my 'learned' advice. She duly asked the question.

"Well," I replied, "there's a well known saying in veterinary which is called the three 'Ts'. You must always ensure that the three Ts are all well looked after; that is the teeth, the toes and the testicles. So I suggest that you check over his teeth and ensure they are in good working order, with no eating problems. Ensure that his feet are properly cared for and he is not lame. Finally, and most importantly, check his testicles. Two nice and big, evenly sized testicles with no abnormalities. Oh yes, testicles are vital to the ram getting steamed up ready for a bout of tupping. Once you have done that you can put him into a field adjacent to the ewes, and this will really get his hormones circulating properly so that he is fully steamed up. Then, at the appropriate time, you can let him out into the field with the ewes and off he'll go tupping away like a Frenchman."

I finished answering my question in, what I thought, was a highly appropriate manner. However, just as I did so, from out of the outside broadcasting units came producers, executive producers, assistant producers, the lot, shaking their heads and hands and looking horrified.

"You can't say 'testicles' on daytime telly, Matt. Get a grip."

What a silly bunch of tuppers, I thought. Sparing the great British public from animal sex when you're doing a show specifically about animals is an onerous task!

The evenings were great fun too. Trude and I were put up in very luxurious hotels, all expenses paid, and we had a great time. She spent hours telling me about her up-bringing in Norway and how she had started out her working career as a milkman. She told me how she had managed to come over to England and eventually get into Bristol vet school. I admired her for her determination and grit, on top of which she was a really lively vivacious girl. As a result of those long summer nights in Chester she has become a great family friend, and still comes to stay with us.

That blistering summer gradually drew to an end, as did the filming. Just in time too, I thought. I'd missed Clare and the kids terribly and was ready to return to normality. I had learnt a lot of things, had a great time, made some friends who are still close even now, and, most interestingly, experienced TV filming that was a million miles away from the casual and informal work that Katie and I did together. I was looking forward to getting back to simplicity. There was one thing I had noticed about the Beeb though, and call me weird for noticing it, but it seemed that all their producers were very short, and only ever wore black! Hmmm.

Filming with the BBC was a great experience and I fear I might have let it go to my head somewhat. Mainly perhaps because I didn't have Clare and my practice there to keep my feet firmly on the ground. The Beeb spent a long time telling me I was extremely good on camera and that I would go a long way. I started to believe them too! They were unanimous that the filming at Chester was just the start of many, many projects to come, saying we would start again in the spring. With

the benefit of hindsight, I now know that that was just TV
hyperbole. Cobblers, to the rest of us. They didn't recommission
the series. I felt very flat and dejected, but had to tell myself
it was their job to 'encourage' their talent. OK, I admit I was
green and fell for it. It brought me back to earth with a quick
thump and I swore that I would always remember that I am
fundamentally, and always will be, a vet! Any TV filming that
came my way was as a result of being that vet, and I was not
going to become rich and famous or a mega-TV star.

Chapter Ten

Although I spend a large amount of my time working with parrots, I have never agreed with people keeping wild animals as pets unless they do it well. Wild animals are just that, they are wild. You might succeed in imprinting them so that they think that you are mum or dad. You might even succeed in socialising them, so they don't tear bits off you every time you go near them. But they are still fundamentally wild animals!

I am passionately against people keeping wild animals that have been caught in the wild. There is a large trade in wild-caught birds, which seem to have paperwork manufactured by unscrupulous dealers pretending the creatures were bred over here.

They do *not* make good pets and tend to be riddled with disease. Occasionally, large shipments of them come over from Belgium, and they end up within the veterinary community as a wave of sick animals. On arrival, they are quarantined for 35 days to ensure that they are not carrying that nasty contagious disease psittacosis. However, to make sure that they survive this and any other diseases they may be carrying, many of the importers put the birds on to antibiotics during this quarantine period. Once finished, they go off to a pet shop and soon end up in people's homes, still diseased! Two weeks later they fall ill, when the drugs' effects have worn off. This, coupled with the stress of being captured and shipped to a foreign country, often causes the birds simply to die.

Birds that have been captured from the wild are easy to spot. First off, they go cheap! And that's not another weak joke. They're like the inexpensive knock-off of home-reared parrots. A bird such as an African grey may only cost, say, 200 pounds. A home-born and hand-reared bird should cost as much as 1000 pounds with a good cage.

Owning a parrot is not for the faint-hearted. Essentially, they're three-year-old children and need to be treated as such. Give them an inch and they will take a mile. They need a lot of attention, and should not spend all day cooped up in a small cage. In fact, their cage should really only act as their bedroom.

Clare and the boys had always wanted a parrot, but I was loath to get one for these very reasons. Despite having her hands full with three children and the rest of the menagerie, Clare still found time to work as a horse vet. But when Peggy left, Lucinda joined us to help look after the children whilst we were at work.

Lucinda has been our right-hand and saviour ever since. She quietly puts everything away and never complains about the ever-increasing mess the Brash mob leave lying around. Lucinda, we decided, could handle a parrot too and so, having adults around 24/7, we started looking for one.

I am offered parrots on a weekly basis, so it was really just a matter of waiting for the right one to come along. You mustn't forget that many of the parrots I'm offered I have treated in the past, and they have long memories and would love to get even with the nasty vet. Rather than playing the friendly pet, they would happily remove chunks from me, given half a chance.

Time went by and none of the parrots I saw were quite right. Then one day I had a very distressed call from a client called Mrs Campbell. I assumed that some ghastly tragedy had befallen her parrot.

I had first met Mrs Campbell's parrot five years earlier, when I had just been thinking of going home on a Friday evening. The phone went.

"My parrot's as sick as a parrot," she said down the line. I chuckled to myself; the old ones are the best.

"I've been to the local vets for the last two days and they don't seem to know what they are doing. Can you help?"

I asked what seemed to be the trouble.

"It's my pet cockatoo, she's passing blood. She's fluffed all her feathers up and is looking very unsteady on her feet."

I sighed, realising that going home for a hot bath was slipping away as a dream. I told her she had better get down here as fast as she could.

"Where are you coming from?" I enquired.

"Leeds."

Leeds, in relation to my clinic, is what they call 'bleeding miles away'. Oh well, I said to myself, at least I'll get lots of paper work done whilst I waited for her.

She arrived with a squeal of tyres and a crunch of the gravel drive and carried her parrot inside.

"What's her name?" I asked.

"Rosie," came the tearful reply.

A woeful sad little face stared up at me. The bird was obviously very ill. Her tail feathers were blood stained and she hung limp in her owner's arms.

"When did she start passing bloody diarrhoea," I asked, an idea coming to me as to what the problem might be.

"On Wednesday," she replied. "We have been renovating our new house and Rosie has been helping."

"What sort of house?"

"An old farm cottage."

Aha! I thought of lead poisoning. "Has she been chewing on anything," I asked.

"Oh yes, she's very good at chewing off the old paint."

This sounded like a classic case of lead poisoning. Old types of paint contained a lot of lead to act as a stabiliser, and in chewing the woodwork Rosie had obviously ingested some of the wretched stuff. It was now poisoning her, so I decided to keep her in. She went onto a drip, which, surprisingly for a parrot, she didn't object to, revealing just exactly how sick she was. I took blood samples, but with it being the weekend we wouldn't have any results until the beginning of following week. The other way to diagnose lead poisoning would have been to X-ray her and look for fragments of heavy metal in her stomach, but I decided against this as the poor creature didn't look strong enough to take it. I would have to go with my hunch. I gave an antidote against lead poisoning to her both by mouth and by injection. Covering antibiotics against infection were also administered.

She was far too sick to stay at the surgery overnight alone, so I took her home. She sat quietly in her cage during the drive home. By the time I got there, the kids had long since gone to bed so it was peaceful for her. I placed her by our bed to watch her and a quiet night was met by a noisy dawn. As the boys flooded into our bedroom early the next day, they were amazed to be met by a ball of white feathers sitting on the table by the bed. Rosie was even more surprised to be meeting boys for the first time. Her umbrella went up and she let out the most incredibly loud ear-splitting/piercing shriek you will ever hear.

Over the rest of the weekend, I spent time trying to find ways of coaxing her to eat, but all to no avail. We tried every trick in the book, but nothing worked. Although she was obviously better, there was no way she was going to eat anything we had to offer.

By Monday I was pulling my hair out, so I rang Mrs Campbell.

"Rosie is much better," I said, "I am sure my diagnosis was right, she is so much better. That said, I simply cannot get her to eat."

"She's very particular about what she eats. It's either Vegemite sandwiches or fresh strawberries. I'll be with you in two hours!"

Mrs Campbell arrived, this time driving a rather grand gold Rolls Royce. She entered the surgery with a plate of Vegemite sandwiches, carefully prepared with the edges trimmed off.

"Oh marvellous, thank you," I said, but Mrs Campbell hadn't finished

"I'll just get the rest."

And off to her car she went. Plates of cucumber, jam and peanut butter sandwiches were followed by a bowl of fresh strawberries, redcurrants and other fruit. Then a basket of mixed macadamia and cashew nuts was finally followed by a whole roast chicken.

"There," she said, "that should keep her going for a day or two, ring me if you need more."

Wow, I thought, staring at the pile of food. If she had only brought a good bottle of wine, I would be home and dry.

Rosie was delighted to see her owner and quickly started on her first course, followed by a fruit cocktail. She finished lunch with some after-dinner nuts. Three days later she went home a happy bird; still on medication and under strict orders not to do any more paint stripping.

Now, many years later, I could hear the tremble of emotion in Mrs Campbell's voice. They were emigrating to Australia and had just discovered that they would not be able to take Rosie with them.

"What are we to do?" she asked. "There must be a way we can get her in. Can't you organise something clever?"

Sadly I could not. Australia is an island with a delicate ecosystem and very few of the nastier diseases. Although cockatoos come from Australia, they are never allowed to go back for fear of what they might bring with them. A better plan than trying to smuggle Rosie into Australia would have to be found.

"Let me think on it," I said. That evening I told Clare, who with her amazing memory could remember the weekend that Rosie had stayed with us.

"We shall have to have her here," she said. "Leave it to me."

And so it came to pass that Rosie moved in with us. I was worried that we'd never be able to keep her in the lifestyle she'd become accustomed to, but we did alright. There's never been a kinder, more gentle bird than she. She adored the children, once she realised that she could shout them down. She enjoyed being groomed by Kipper the dog, and loved to stalk the poor cat Curlew. However, she never grew out of her love of chewing paint off woodwork; thankfully, ours is lead free.

Chapter Eleven

From an early stage of filming with Katie, I realised that many of the things that came naturally to me were a mystery to her. Standard veterinary procedures and tricks of the trade that I didn't think about, I just got on with. So if they were a mystery to her, then they'd be a mystery to the general public. You're probably the same with your job: you just do it, but to anyone watching it's both fascinating and baffling. We also found that if I did explain exactly what I was doing, it made it all the easier for Katie to film it.

One of the aspects of my work Katie thought fascinating was putting animals under anaesthetic. Anaesthetising animals is an area where zoo and exotic animal veterinary differs markedly from pet veterinary. When, say, dogs or cats come in for an operation, they are given a pre-med made up of a sedative and painkiller. This pre-med often contains an opiate, a drug related to morphine, so basically the animal just doesn't care about being at the vets after that. About half an hour later, they are induced. In other words they are anaesthetised using an intravenous liquid. Once asleep, they are connected to anaesthetic machines, and breathe a mixture of oxygen and anaesthetic gases. The process is quick, non-stressful, and easily controlled, and fundamentally the same as with humans.

With zoo animals it's a different matter altogether. The problems we encounter are as diverse as the creatures we treat, and we spend many hours finding new ways round the difficulties we encounter. One problem that they all have in common is that they are buggers to catch. They all know me, and hate me! And the more intelligent the animal, the more they love to hate me and the greater their desire to take a chunk out of me. Getting hold of them can become a dangerous game. A battle of half-wits, my wife calls it.

Whilst they spend their visit avoiding being trapped, caught or cornered, I spend my time working out how to make the whole experience as relaxed as possible. The reasons are logical. A stressed animal is far more likely to injure itself trying to escape, or even drop dead from a heart attack. Sadly, animals can die hours after a procedure from a condition called capture myopathy. This condition is similar in many ways to having excessive cramp; cramp so bad that you end up being unable to stand, and the damage to the muscles ultimately damages the liver and kidneys.

Heat stroke in the animals is another major problem, so careful consideration is always given to the climatic conditions. I tend not to even attempt to operate on very hot days. Luckily, being in Yorkshire, hot days are as rare as rocking horse droppings.

With the smaller animals, such as little monkeys, meerkats and birds, we catch them by hand, often employing a net or the old faithful towel. Oh, and occasionally thick gloves, the sturdiness of which is scientifically matched to how hard the devils can bite.

With the larger animals we have to get anaesthetics into them from a distance, by cunning. Or as cunning as one can get with a dart gun or a great big blowpipe.

When I had first started at the Zoo back in 1991, we had none of the complicated and sophisticated equipment that we have today. In fact, the only reliable way we had to get an anaesthetic drug into an animal was Neville's rifle. Non-anaesthetics, antibiotics and vitamins and the like, we have to get in with guile and scheming. Hiding them in their food, basically. This means the animals are often given unexpected treats, which occasionally have medicine in them as well. Peanut butter and jam sandwiches work particularly well for the polar bears, while molasses in the dried food work better for the bison. The monkeys go crazy for fruit-based drinks such as Ribena, and the parrots like the odd bowl of porridge. With them trained to eat these tasty morsels, it means that if they ever get an infection we will be able to get treatments into them easily. Many of the diseases in, say, monkeys, are the same as people get, so not only do we have to try to ensure that we don't pick up diseases from them, but that they don't pick up anything from us. Even a common cold can prove fatal in some of the primates. But the success rate is limited with this treat method. A lot of drugs we use are too bitter and nasty tasting and you can never be sure the animal has got it all.

You must remember that there is never any chance of us being able to examine many of the animals conscious: the rotten polar bear incident is proof enough of that. The only ones I have ever been able to handle conscious have been small enough to hold in the palm of my hand and an elephant. I don't have really, really big hands; elephants are just very trusting creatures.

Everything else needs to be knocked out. To do this we used to have to use Neville and his rifle. The problem with Neville's rifle was that it was extremely noisy. It let off such an almighty bang when he fired it, I used to wonder whether the animals would pass out from shock. Certainly, after firing it there was always a silence that was so loud you could have heard a pin drop. The bang was so powerful, we used to have to wait a few minutes for that annoying ringing to disappear from our ears. If the shot didn't work first time, you might as well give up and go home as there was never to be a second chance that day. Every man and beast would be on tenterhooks for hours! The rifle was ideal to use outside for large hoof stock, like zebra and bison, but too much trouble for inside work.

The purchase of a primitive blowpipe was, ironically, a major leap forward in technology for us. This was as simple a device as it sounds. It was a piece of plastic piping into which you put your charged dart and then, pointing it at your target, you blew. The better your puff, the faster the dart flew and the greater your chances of success. Sadly, I've never been much of a puff, and Nelson the chimp was the one to find me out.

The first animal I had to try my new toy out on was perhaps the wrong choice. Nelson was the old daddy of the chimps. He was a wise old bird then, and 15 years on he is wiser still. Nelson knew from the first moment he saw me that I was a vet. I was the enemy and not one of his friends. He welcomed me on my visits to see him with his great party trick. Whilst pretending to be distracted, he would keep a close beady eye on me. As soon as I wasn't looking at him, he would poo in his hand and flick it at me with astonishing accuracy. There was many a time he had managed to get me on the back of my neck just as I was leaving his indoor enclosure. He hasn't managed to get me for a number of years now, but I won't let complacency kill the vet.

When he cut his hand badly and needed stitches, I felt this was the ideal opportunity to try out my new blowpipe. Having loaded a dart, and having trapped Nelson in one of the smaller overnight cages, I carefully walked up to the edge of the cage with the blowpipe concealed behind my back. Nelson watched me, waiting for his chance. My production of a long, thin bright-yellow plastic tube that I then pointed at him was, however, not in his game plan at all. As I pointed it at him, he moved carefully over to the other side of the cage. This meant I had to remove my pipe from between the bars and reposition it to point it at him. He would then move again. This slow drama continued for the next two hours, with neither of us giving way and me never getting anywhere near a chance of a shot. Nelson got bored and decided he was not going to move. I eventually got a good shot; I took aim, breathed deeply and blew, firing the dart at him. Quick as a flash, the hairy little so-and-so spun round, caught the dart in mid-flight and hurled it back at me. I had to duck sharpish and heard the thing whiz past my ear only inches away. Nelson is fast, but I'm a trained vet and fully paid-up coward, so I'm faster. I got him in the end, and managed to close his wound with a few stitches, but he knew about the blowpipe now.

The blowpipe was not going to be much use on chimps. We would need to upgrade.

The arrival of the dart rifle made life much easier. This was a rifle that worked on compressed gas and so was silent. Not only that, it had a laser beam direction finder. What a joy! Now I could point the gun almost lackadaisically at an animal, using the laser beam to find the right target, and fire. A silent puff and I had got them. This completely revolutionised anaesthetising the animals at the Zoo.

Mind you, it wasn't all easy and straight forward, and knocking out zebras always makes my hands shake. This is because we use an anaesthetic called Immobilon. It's a nasty cocktail of two drugs, and whilst it is very good at dropping down zebras, it is fatal to humans. In fact, it is so dangerous that a few drops on a cut on your skin will kill you within a couple of minutes unless you manage to get the antidote into yourself quickly. So when we use the drug we always carry the antidote with us, ready prepared in a syringe. We always have someone close to hand ready to plunge it into you should the unthinkable happen. Mind you, if we both get it on us we're toast.

The first time I had to use Immobilon, whilst filming with Katie, I was doubly apprehensive. Not only was I planning to use Immobilon, but I would have the added distraction of Katie. But she, as ever, was the consummate professional. As I pulled on two layers of gloves, one extra for luck, she gently asked me to talk through what I was doing and why. She had never filmed me darting anything and so was intrigued with what I was up to.

I found this gentle line of questioning helpful, as it stopped me worrying. I began to explain each step as we went in a methodical manner. The dose for a zebra is small; they only need about one cubic centimetre. This has to be carefully loaded into the syringe and the remaining space filled with sterile water. Too much air in the dart could cause it to bounce off, or accidentally inject air into the muscle. A special needle with a small hole in the side of the shaft is then put on, and an even smaller rubber sleeve slid over the hole. This stops the liquid coming out when the other end of the dart is pressurised with air. When the needle penetrates the skin, the small rubber sleeve is pushed back exposing the hole in the needle. This pressurised air then forces the drug into the muscle. Finally, a flight feather is put on to assist the dart's smooth flight through the air.

The dart is obviously highly dangerous and must be put into the barrel of the dart gun immediately. This makes it safe and keeps it out of harm's way. Only when we have pressurised the gun does it become a dangerous weapon.

Katie filmed the procedure and continued rolling as I carefully lined the laser up with the rump of the zebra. A small pop, the zebra jumped up slightly, and looked round to see the dart with its bright red feather sticking out of its bottom. This new method of darting was easy! In this particular case, we had been darting the zebra so that I cold remove a small tumour from his flank. Whilst asleep, we trimmed his feet and checked his teeth. Once finished, we reversed the anaesthetic and within minutes he was up and standing, albeit looking a bit groggy. Over the years we have used the dart rifle many, many times, and its silence and accuracy have improved our success rates in many cases, by minimising the stress to the animals.

Only once have I had to use Immobilon without the dart gun, and that was when I had to put the old bull elephant to sleep. There were two elephants when I first started working at the Zoo. Jangoli was the younger of the two, a mere stripling in her 30s. She was unique in that she had broken her tail many years earlier in an argument with another elephant over something or other; you know what women are like. Where the tail bent there was a sore that, try as we might, we could never get to heal. My predecessors had tried everything under the sun, so I was determined to be the one who succeeded. Creams, salves and ointments were applied on a daily basis and, although we could keep it under control, we could never get it to actually heal. She didn't mind the keepers looking at it, but she did mind me; after all, I was the vet!

It being her tail, this meant me tiptoeing my way round the back to have a look. This makes even the most trusting of creatures a tad uneasy. Elephants don't really kick out, but they can throw their weight about. She knew that, when you were behind her, she could just slowly push you up against a wall and give you a little crush, just for fun like, but it can be quite frightening.

The trick in examining her was to ensure that you always looked at her tail with a corner of the room behind you, so that when she pushed you backwards there was just space enough for you to hide in the corner, whilst hoping she didn't pass wind.

Her mate was older and began to lose weight. Blood tests revealed that he had kidney failure and, despite lots of treatment, he deteriorated until sadly we decided that the time had come for him to be put to sleep.

Letting any animal go is always traumatic, but doesn't normally present any great logistical problems. But putting an elephant to sleep is another matter. Weighing in at several tons, this was not going to be easy. The sheer volume of anaesthetic itself was going to be massive. Luckily elephants are like people and are highly sensitive to Immobilon. A small teaspoonful would suffice.

Planning was important. We decided that it would be best done when there were no members of the public about, for safety and decorum's sake; so we decided on seven a.m. There would then be the small problem of moving the corpse using tractors and loading him into a large wagon using a crane. Once he was dead, I would need to carry out a post mortem at the local abattoir, and after this he would need to go for cremation.

On the day itself everything went exactly as planned. I placed a small catheter in his ear vein and then quickly injected the Immobilon, making sure that none went on me. I then hopped quickly out of the way, trying to make sure that he didn't land on me. In a few seconds he was swaying and then he gradually subsided to the floor. We allowed his friend and companion to see him before we took him away. As she looked at him, a small tear rolled down her cheek. This left us speechless and all the more heartbroken.

I confirmed with the post mortem that he had had cancer of the kidneys, and so we had done the right thing. Next, however, we had to dispose of his body.

There was really only one place big enough to cope, and that was a large industrial abattoir in Lincolnshire. The following day he was taken down there to be cremated. But he was so large that he gummed all their machinery up and brought the place to a grinding stand-still for several days whilst they fixed their contraptions. This led to a change in policy regarding the death of large mammals in the UK; they are now buried.

Chapter Twelve

One group of animals I have never had to use the dart gun on is the wallabies. They are miniature versions of kangaroos, originating from the outback of Australia. Flamingo Land has about a dozen of these peaceful-looking animals. Peaceful, until they're cornered that is, then all hell breaks loose; and they can bounce and kick above their weight.

Like all marsupials, they have an unusual birthing process. When a joey is born, approximately just one centimetre long, it crawls up its mother's fur into her pouch. There it latches onto a teat and suckles milk. Joeys can stay there for many months, more than a year in some species. It can, however, look a bit odd when a developed two-foot baby wallaby, standing upright, is suddenly startled and dives head first inside its mother. Kicking and punching its way round until it is head-up and facing the right way. Ouch! The wallabies are a low maintenance exhibit for the Zoo, breeding quietly away in the corner near the old polar bear enclosure. So I was surprised one morning to have a call from Alison, the Zoo's veterinary nurse, regarding them. The Zoo has had a nurse for a long time, a useful addition to the team as he or she can administer drugs under my direction and look at animals for me when I am not actually there.

Alison said that a joey had been rejected by its mother; something that had never happened before. So Katie and I hopped into the car and headed straight off to the Zoo.

A small bay wallaby was lying wrapped in blankets and sitting on a hot water bottle. For some reason he had fallen or climbed out of his mother's pouch during the night, and now mum didn't want anything to do with him. As luck would have it, Alison was Australian and had worked in a wildlife centre there for a spell, so had more of an inkling regarding how to set about looking after a baby marsupial than the rest of us.

"You can't give them milk," she said, in her broad Aussie accent. "It makes them go blind." Well, you learn something new each day!

I pointed out that they drink their mother's milk whilst still in the pouch.

"Oh yeah, but it's not cow's milk, is it? Different thing altogether," she said with authority.

I nodded and stuck out my bottom lip, like I always do when I learn something new. I asked what we should give her to eat then, eager to learn more.

Alison looked at her feet and shuffled them. "I dunno. That's the only thing I remember about looking after them."

We were going to have to do some research. This is a common problem with zoo animals. There is without doubt infinitely more that is unknown than is known. Yet the knowledge that is out there amongst the zoo community is vast, and somewhere somebody would know what to feed a wallaby. This is where the beauty of the Internet truly comes into play.

First, we had to set about getting this little youngster stabilised. He was cold, dehydrated and failing.

We gave him some fluids intravenously, and some covering antibiotics as his breathing wasn't as good as it should be. We then tried to teach him to drink from an artificial teat. I had brought some lammac feeders; these are small glass bottles with tiny, tiny teats that we use for feeding kittens. Initially, we gave him fluids in the form of sugars and minerals. He didn't think much of this, but Alison persevered and soon managed to get enough down him that he began to look brighter.

Alison discovered from friends in Australia that the ideal milk was goat's milk, and that the main problem with cow's milk was the lactose. Wallabies are lactose intolerant. Ah ha, now we really were learning something new!

Within days, Alison had managed to settle herself and her new charge into a routine. He lived in a handbag that was carried around on her shoulders. The bag had a large folded blanket, surrounded by two hot water bottles. This successfully mimicked a mother's pouch, but perhaps was not as humid, as he began to develop skin problems. The blanket was swapped for an artificial fur and this all settled down.

Alison's patience was phenomenal. In the wild, a joey will suckle from its mother's teat pretty well all the time; only when they are older, upon leaving the pouch, does their rate of feeding finally slow down. Alison had to mimic this, and so fed small amounts of goat's milk as often as she could. Initially this was hourly, day and night. How she had the patience was completely beyond me. The little joey soon got a name, Beanie, and Katie was delighted. Beanie and his new mum were so photogenic, it was going to look lovely on the telly.

Alison and Beanie bonded very quickly and soon became completely inseparable. This had its advantages, and its disadvantages. Whenever there was the slightest breakdown in hygiene, or if he drank too much too quickly, he would get diarrhoea. *E. coli* diarrhoea, the scourge of butchers in the UK, was a potentially fatal problem, so the slightest loose motion would have Alison panicking on the phone to enquire whether we should put him on antibiotics. We had to be careful, as long term exposure to antibiotics can have detrimental effects. It was a steep learning curve for us all, but it worked and Beanie grew quickly and happily.

Unfortunately we were all putting our heads in the sand, really. Wallabies in a zoo are still wild animals, and to hand-rear one can lead to a lot of complications and potential problems later on in life. But, on the other hand, we couldn't have let the little mite just starve to death. As he grew he became too heavy for Alison to carry around and she had to leave him in the hospital at the keeper's yard. He used to sit there waiting for mum's return. He would need to go back with the others soon. As he was so firmly imprinted on people now, we decided that he had to be castrated. Surgery on any wild animal always has risks, but elective surgery, where I have decided that we should operate rather than operating when an animal injures itself, always carries an extra responsibility. If an animal is hurt or ill and then died under anaesthetic, then at least we had tried to save it. However, if I were to lose one that I had elected to operate on then that would be unbearable. So the decision to castrate Beanie wasn't taken lightly. Wallabies don't react well to anaesthetics and, as this one was only five or six months old, it would be twice as difficult.

Katie was filming, of course, so I can't begin to describe the extra pressure I was under. He was put under using Isoflorane anaesthetic. It is such a safe gas because the animal goes to sleep quickly and as soon as you stop the flow of gas the animal wakes up. Speed is vital, as keeping stress to a minimum is paramount when dealing with wild animals.

An extra pressure I could have avoided was the fact that I used Alison as my veterinary nurse for the operation. With hindsight, I should have brought one of the nurses up from the surgery, but I didn't think of it at the time. Of course Alison was emotionally attached to Beanie, so she was going to be pretty twitchy herself throughout the operation.

Beanie went to sleep easily but, after placing a tube in his trachea to ensure he breathed a mixture of oxygen and anaesthetic gas, he quickly decided to stop breathing and seemed to die on us. On closer inspection I found he was still with us, just.

At times like that it's very easy to just call off the operation and bring the animal round. But he was there, I was there, and the operation needed to be done. With Alison artificially breathing for him, I ploughed on. The operation was over quickly and he began to wake up. Katie had been filming so quietly and professionally I had almost forgotten she was there.

As we climbed back into my car to return to the surgery, she turned and said that it had looked a bit stressful. She could only see the half of it. To have lost little Beanie after Alison had looked after him day and night with such tender loving care ... well it didn't bear thinking about.

Once he had finally grown up and left the 'pouch', he began to be reintroduced to the rest of the group. This involved Alison leaving him out with the others for short periods of time. The rest of the time he would spend in the keeper's yard, hopping around with all his friends, watching them work and learning how to weld and prepare food. He was a cheerful chappy who was fun to have around, so it was with mixed feelings when we realised he was getting on with the other wallabies and could now go back with them permanently.

I rather think the management breathed a sigh of relief at this point, thinking perhaps their keepers would get back to work now.

Whilst filming our programme, I was not able to take the camera with me on all my calls. One such call was to visit the owls that were being used for the filming of a Harry Potter story. I knew of the books, as my kids were big fans of them. I expected to arrive on some lavish, Hollywood-style film set with extras, cameramen, directors and huge stars milling about. I couldn't have been more wrong.

I had been asked to go to Newcastle, where the birds were being trained. Jacqui, our practice secretary, had taken directions, and as I arrived in a dingy little industrial estate that looked old and abandoned, like something out of *Scooby Doo,* I thought I really must be in the wrong place.

A quick phone call to Jacqui confirmed that her directions were perfect, of course. I was just being an idiot. I rang the mobile phone they had given me, to discover that they were all off site, having lunch at the local pub.

"Come and join us, Matt."

I wound my way deeper into Newcastle, and found the pub they were propped up in. I was relieved that what had been looking like a wild goose chase was over.

"Join us," they said.

I pulled up a chair and explained that I had been convinced I was in the wrong place, having seen how derelict the site was.

"Just wait and see," came the reply.

After lunch, in convoy we drove back to the site. On arriving they must have had a remote control gadget in their car, as large hangar doors scrolled upwards, to reveal the most amazing Aladdin's cave of state-of-the-art cameras, editing machines and all manner of electronic wizardry. I later found out that they deliberately made the place look desolate to dissuade the nosey public from poking about.

In one corner of the vast hangar were the animals. Tawny and barn owls were busy being trained to carry scrolls in their mouths, whilst eagle owls and large giant toads stood around on perches or in tanks. I wondered how exactly they trained giant toads, and what exactly they trained them to do. The birds, however, were not well. Although they were flying, it was not with their normal pizzazz. Some were looking hunched up and the two barn owls were breathing heavily.

At closer examination, and on listening to their chests, I could hear a lot of sounds that shouldn't be there. After quizzing them about the birds, I discovered that they had all travelled up from the south of England over the last few days in hot dusty boxes. I suspected that they had aspergillosis, a fungal disease that commonly affects birds' airways.

The producers were counting on the birds being in good health, as filming was due to start quite soon; but I had bad news for them. Unless we were able to get the birds over their illness, they could not be used during the filming. I had a week to try and get them better. The first move was to take blood samples and get those off to a lab for analysis. The results came back two days later, confirming that the birds had an infection. Also, the barn owls had a nasty blood-born parasite disorder called leucocytozoonosis. This is a blood disorder in which a parasite attacks the white cells, leaving the bird's immune system to fail. It was a Friday by now, and the birds had moved location down to the actual set.

We began treatment right away, and I spent the weekend worrying that the birds would not get better. Or, even worse, my treatment would kill them. Happily, when I drove up to the location above Pickering on the Monday, you could see the improvement in the birds. They had responded fantastically, so the filming could commence. The training must have upped a gear too and I was so proud one year later when I saw the film. To think that I had treated those magnificent, magical birds as they swooped and dived around Hogwarts carrying their scrolls. Later I was told that the director of the film had decided that computer-generated birds looked more natural on screen than real birds. The only time the genuine owls are seen is when they're on someone's arm. That burst my bubble, I can tell you. Next thing they'll be telling us that ruddy Dobby the house-elf was computer-generated as well! Pah!

Chapter Thirteen

I had been disappointed that I hadn't heard any more from the BBC. I felt that if they had changed their mind about filming another series then they should at least have had the decency to let me know. But it did serve to remind me that I was fundamentally a vet, and always would be. So our halcyon days in Yorkshire went back to normal and Katie and I carried on filming at the Zoo, whenever I went.

In the April of that year I got quite a shock when I noticed on the message pad at work that a producer from the BBC had rung. Would I ring her back?

I 'ummed and 'ahed about whether to ring them or not and tried to tell myself to play it cool and let them come back to me. But, of course, a bit like the cat and cream, I had to see what they wanted, so I rang.

Although they had decided not to film another series of *Vets To The Rescue* (run out of lycra, I thought to myself), they had decided to film a different series called *Vets In The Country*.

"Oooh, what's that about then?" I asked, failing to hide my excitement.

"Well, fundamentally, it's about some vets, and they're in the country this time," came the slow reply.

Play it cool, I told myself again.

The wonderful Trude Mostue, now a good friend to both Clare and me, was to be at the helm. The new series was to be based at a vet's somewhere in the countryside, and they wanted to know if we would be willing to assist filming. I put the phone down feeling very thrown. I would have to talk it through with my colleagues, and I was wondering how on earth I would manage to film both *Zoo Vet* and for the BBC. However, Stuart was up for a laugh and, as the filming of *Zoo Vet* was still based solely at the Zoo, and would soon be over, hey why not give it a go.

They came over for a chat, still all dressed in black and still all only five foot tall (I'm sure they're clones). We talked about filming, they met Stuart, and we all had a drive around the countryside so they could get a feel for the area. They said they were looking at several other locations to film and would be in touch once they had decided where they were going to shoot.

One week later they returned to tell us how very lucky we were, they had decided to film with us at the surgery in Stamford Bridge. They assured us that disturbance would be minimal and that we would hardly notice them being there. Being used to Katie, and somewhat naive about TV, I believed them! Stuart and the rest of the staff believed me. Oops.

So the following month the Beeb moved in, and boy how they moved in! They rented a farm nearby and set it up like it was the control panel in the starship Enterprise. The 'just a few people' soon grew to three camera crews, each crew being made up of a camera person, a sound recorder, a director and a handful of those people who are always present on filming projects but never seem to do anything (I think they're execs or something). They would ring at all times of the day and night to ask what we were doing, and why we were doing what we were doing, and could they come and film it. If there weren't enough sick animals, they wanted to know why not and where were they? All in all, they turned our lives upside down. Despite my arguments that filming would be much easier if there was just a single camera person, they insisted that the only way to make a film was to have the full crew of three. This made working in our rather small consulting rooms very tight indeed. Particularly when clients who brought their pets to the surgery also needed to bring their five children with them.

The Beeb kept wearing their compulsory black, and talked rapidly to each other down mobile phones that were so small I feared somebody's hamster might choke on one. They changed their mind continuously as to exactly what they wanted to film. They'd film clients and their pets, building their expectations up that they'd get on the telly, then out of the blue completely change their minds and stop filming. We spent that summer constantly worrying that they would upset our clients, and so Stuart and I spent our evenings ringing people to check they were OK.

Andrew, based over at the Strensall surgery, seemed to have the best idea of how to handle them. On a daily basis the Beeb would ring him to see if he was doing anything interesting. He would reply, on a daily basis, in his dry Scottish manner, "Na, dull as ditchwater this lot. Sorry". They left him alone completely!

I am perhaps sounding a bit caustic about them, and that is not entirely fair. They were lovely people, who had a job to do. The one thing they could do was to pour on the charm. They oozed their way into our quiet corner of Yorkshire and charmed the pants off everyone. The very fact that it was the BBC seemed to carry some amazing kudos, and nobody seemed to mind what they did. If they had actually been able to speak to animals, à la Dr Doolittle, then I am quite sure that a calving cow would have happily stopped straining until the cameras got there. A cockatoo in surgery would wake up and say, "You know love, I think I could do that better". And Nelson the chimp, just as he's about to chuck a handful of his own poo at me, would ask them, "What's my motivation again, lovey?"

Once they had set up their base camp properly, Trude arrived and we began filming. The producers wanted Trude to fit right in as one of the boys. Well, they had missed a slight point I thought, but I knew what they meant.

The first day of filming began with the two of us taking a trip to Janie Bell's to operate on her newly purchased llama, Todd. Another example of when not quite everything goes according to plan.

In any profession there are insults that mean very little to those outside of that industry. One plumber might say to another, "You couldn't set the maximum inlet pressure on a BSPF pressure reducing valve, you muppet!" Or one astronaut might sarcastically berate another with, "You do realise it's the pointy end of the rocket that goes up?" I sincerely hope I have coined the veterinary profession's most scathing rebuke, "You couldn't castrate a llama."

Janie had acquired a llama but didn't want anymore, and asked if we could do something about it. Breeding control is imperative with wild animals, and even llamas, placid and daft looking as they are, can become quite aggressive chaps if their urges aren't quelled. The operation was arranged and the motley crew of sound recordists, spare camera personnel *et al.* rolled up. Janie had been pre-warned that we were filming, but I don't think anyone had told the poor old llama. I checked him over and in the sure knowledge that everything was where it was meant to be, anaesthetised him. The cameras were rolling, so I was trying to be the consummate vet in control of the situation.

I told Trude I could feel the two testicles, and two smaller ones. What? Four gonads! I made an incision and began poking about trying to find some answers. I took hold of one of the larger lumps and tried to draw it out. It was then I discovered the two larger lumps were actually the animal's penis. It has an S-shaped, or sigmoid, one, and the lumps were the curves. And there was I trying to pull it out of an incision. I quickly put it back, to spare mine and the llama's blushes, but could I find the testicles? They just weren't there! I presumed the two smaller lumps were them, as llama nuts are very small, but no. The lumps, in my opinion, were the scar tissue remaining after the animal had *already* been castrated. Janie had been told the llama had never been done, it was only a year old, but there were no gonads to be found anywhere. So, in summary, in front of a film crew, I found two sets of testicles, tried to remove a penis by mistake, then lost all four nuts and wasted the llama's entire morning. A few years later the BBC made a series called *It Shouldn't Happen To*, which featured on-screen blunders of weather people and presenters and the like. When they did one on TV vets I got to relive my llama drama in full colour on prime-time telly. Thanks, Beeb.

Unlike filming for *Zoo Vet*, where there was just me and a camera lady, there were so many people involved with *Vets In The Country* that, invariably, the animals misbehaved or something went awry. This led to endless repeating of walking through doors, opening car doors and pretending to arrive, or depart, from a visit. The series was to be 25 half-hour episodes long, so a lot of footage was needed.

Language and name problems can sometime raise a smile, but they're usually the type of anecdote that ends with a stony response from the person you're telling it to, and you saying, "You had to be there."

Trude Mostue is, of course, Norwegian, and sometimes our multi-layered classification of British wildlife can be a bit befuddling. It fuddles me! Early in the filming, one day a client arrived with an owl for me to examine. It was a small species of native owl called, imaginatively, a Little Owl. We were filming in front of the large crew when Trude walked in and asked me, for the benefit of the viewers at home, what type of bird I was looking at. The conversation went something like this:

"Hi Matt. What sort of bird are you looking at?"

"It's a Little Owl."

"It is, isn't it. What type is it?"

"A Little Owl."

"Oh, so it's a baby. I see. What type of baby owl is it?"

"A Little Owl."

"Yes, but what sort of little owl?"

"The species is called Little Owl!"

"Ooh, is it a little Little Owl then?"

"Nope, pretty big for a Little Owl really!"

Well, the audience thought it was funny. But you did have to be there.

Chapter Fourteen

As part of my brief from the BBC they wanted me to take Trude out on visits to interesting clients. These were always fun. Trude works mainly with small animals and had not been out looking at larger ones since her days at Bristol University. Perhaps the most memorable was the trip to visit the ostriches belonging to Chris.

Ostrich farming had taken off in Yorkshire in a big way in the mid to late 1990s. The ostrich is an unusual bird, originating from the southern end of Africa, and there are two main subspecies, the blue and black ostriches. They were being farmed in the UK as part of Britain's obsession with health and good eating. Ostriches produce a good amount of high-quality meat that's low in cholesterol and fat. At one point I was looking after 18 ostrich farms in the small area around Stamford Bridge. Not all the farms were very big, some only had a few birds, but Derwent Ostriches had loads. This farm seemed a natural candidate to take Trude and the BBC to visit.

The farming of ostriches is simple. They are first kept as trios, one male to two females, and are then kept as larger groups or flocks. Each female ostrich will start laying eggs in the early spring and could, theoretically, lay two or even three eggs per week over a long summer. A really prolific ostrich may lay nearly 100 eggs in a season. As you can imagine, that's a lot of eggs. And if they all hatch out into ostriches, they could fetch around 700 pounds each! That's good money in anyone's books.

I had been looking after Chris's ostriches for a number of years before the BBC came along, and so I knew him well. Initially Chris had had problems keeping the young chicks alive. Essentially they are wild animals, even if they are being farmed for their meat in the English countryside, and as such they still have very wild instincts. In the wild they like to spend their time together as a group; the herd instinct of protection comes in to play. The young are often corralled together and are precocial, in other words can feed for themselves as soon as they are born. The big problem is that they do like to imprint on a mother figure very soon after they hatch out of their eggs. Obviously in the wild, this would be an adult ostrich, but in captivity it is the farmer. When they are left alone, without their mother figure, they feel vulnerable and scared. Just like we humans, they count on mum and dad to keep them safe.

You cannot spend all day long with a newly hatched ostrich, it just isn't practical; a farmer has other things he or she needs to go and do. In the early years of farming, Chris had lost a lot of chicks dying from secondary disease as a result of stress, and I had had to come up with a way of minimising that stress. Eventually we came up with a formula that seemed to work. If the farmer always wore a blue overall to work, then we could peg out an identical overall on the wall. This, combined with a cardboard cutout of his face and a pair of wellies at the bottom, may just fool the ostriches. After all their brains, even once fully grown, are still only the size of a walnut.

To complete the charade, we then left the radio on all the time, tuned to Radio 4, so that there was a lot of talking. It worked; the baby ostriches were fooled, and happily went back to eating and growing.

That had been several years ago, and Chris's ostrich farming enterprise had grown significantly in size. He had nearly 100 breeding adult birds, made up of 70 females and 30 males.

They all lived together in a field near the main farmhouse, and every morning Chris would drive round the field to collect the eggs from the sand-based communal nests the ostriches made for themselves.

We had a filming idea that involved Trude and I going with Chris in his open-backed pick-up truck to collect the eggs. However, I had forgotten the extensive BBC crew that always followed Trude around. On arrival at the farm, Chris packed Trude, myself, camera crew, sound crew, etc. into the back of the pick-up. Before we set off, he carefully warned us not to stray too far as the ostriches could be a bit protective.

This was a major understatement. On arriving at the field, the first task was to open the gate to allow the pick-up in. On the other side of the gate were the quite menacing looking, seven-foot tall ostriches patrolling the perimeter of their field to ward of predators. They reminded me, worryingly, of velociraptors from *Jurassic Park*. We reminded them of intruders.

Chris shouted back from his truck, "Matt, you wouldn't pop out and open the gate would you?"

"Of course," I replied, then turned to see if Trude wanted to, as she was the star of the show and I was a bit frightened.

She didn't look keen, so I hopped off the back of the truck. As I passed Chris's open window, he leant out and passed me a large stick.

"Watch that one there, he can be it a bit funny. Oh, and that one as well; actually watch all the males, they can be a bit tricky at this time of year," he said nonchalantly.

I carefully nudged the gate open, keeping a close, watchful eye on the big birds, as they did much the same to me.

As soon as Chris was through the gate, I slammed it back into place and dived back into the truck. I had seen at first hand what their powerful legs could do and I was having none of it. A year before, I had come out to look at an ostrich with a sore eye. We had managed to handle the bird into a crush and then cover its head with a sock to keep it calm. At this point it had lashed forwards with its foot, trying to get rid of me. It missed me and caught its own neck, ripping a two-foot long gash down the side. I then spent the next two hours stitching the wound back up together again. Well, I did say their brains are only the size of a walnut! I was going nowhere near those feet. No siree!

We drove round the field, collecting eggs as we went, like bizarre Easter bunnies. The ostriches followed us as a predator follows a prey. There was no doubt that, at any given moment, with just a step out of place, they would have fallen upon us, ripping the flesh from our bones, and devouring us. Oh, oops, they're herbivorous and like eating grass and grain. So they probably wouldn't have actually eaten us, maybe just beaten us up a bit for stealing their eggs, but that's exactly what it felt like they were thinking at the time. Typically, none of the others offered to hop out of the truck to lend a hand. Strange that. The BBC is the finest news agency on the planet and brings us stories from the most terrifying war-torn areas of the world, but stick 'em in a field with some ostriches and they might as well be local news. It was eerie and had flashbacks of Hitchcock's film *The Birds*.

As we completed the circuit of the field, the ostriches seemed to get bolder; either that or they were getting more and more outraged. Eventually they came up to the side of the truck and started pecking at us. The camera crew shrank lower and lower into the truck and I am sure would quite happily have fled. Mind you, that looked like the more dangerous option.

Once we had left the field behind, there was a collective sigh of relief. We had collected nearly 20 eggs. It had been like some cruel Japanese game show. The eggs were then cleaned and placed in racks in a giant incubator for the next 30 days before hatching out.

Trude, throughout, had stayed silent, and I never did discover whether she had enjoyed her close-call with the ostriches. My guess is no.

Sadly, the great British beef-eating public didn't take to eating ostrich. I could understand. The only time we had any was when one of the ostriches had escaped and had to be shot. The farmer kindly offered us a steak, which we duly cooked. Clare described it best as tasting like "iffy chicken that had been raised on a guano-infested island". But perhaps that was because I had performed the autopsy just prior to cooking it!

With the decline of the ostrich market, Chris decided to off-load some of his birds. The market was still vibrant in Italy, so he sold 30 to them. Part of the deal was that the birds would be scanned first, to check that they were fertile females and had good egg-laying potential. This was January, and just about the time when they start to lay their eggs. Chris rounded the 30 birds up, and I went along to scan their ovaries.

It's a relatively simple procedure, as God designed ostriches so that they have no feathers on their flanks. I scanned all the birds, rejecting a few that had no apparent active ovaries. It took the next few months to arrange transport and export licences and such. When all this was sorted, I visited Chris again and checked the birds over to ensure they were fit to travel. All seemed ticketyboo and off they went.

Unfortunately, during this time, the ostrich farming industry was beginning to collapse in Italy as well. The Italian farmer buying them began to get cold feet and was desperately looking for a way out of the deal. First, he announced that we had sent him the wrong ostriches. He had ordered pure blue ostriches and claimed these were hybrid, blue ostriches crossed with black ostriches. Chris was adamant they were as pure as could be, by top-notch UK standards, so his argument fell down there. Next, he complained that they were not breeding properly and some of the birds were not laying eggs. I wasn't surprised, as the birds had been kept in a shed for the last three months and were probably shaken up at having had to travel all that way. Chris calmed the irate little man down by sending a tray of 100 ostrich eggs. A large omelette I quipped: how the hell do you send eggs through the post!

I thought no more about the ostriches until later that year when I received a phone call from DEFRA. They asked if I had exported a number of ostriches to Italy earlier that year and I answered truthfully. They told me there were three men in dark suits looking for me. Why me? It wasn't my business transaction. It turned out that when I had signed the export paper work, I had signed as a ministry vet. The address of the exporting ministry for our area is in Northallerton, and so that is where they went when looking for me.

"Is there a problem with the paper work?" I asked.

"Well, no not really," they replied, "It's just that the farmer wants his money back."

I explained it wasn't my problem and they decided to contact Chris.

I heard no more until Chris rang the following week. He claimed he had had the strangest visitation. Three men in dark suits from Italy! One short with glasses and two large men carrying brief cases. They wanted their money back! I was so glad they hadn't turned up on my doorstep, I've seen too many mafia films! Apparently they gave him 24 hours to think about it. Images of severed ostrich heads on his pillow flashed before my eyes. I asked what he did.

"Well what do you bloody think!? I gave the money back to them of course!"

Slowly the whole story came out. The money behind the ostrich farming plan in Italy was mafia money. When the whole enterprise went belly up, they wanted their money back and thus came to England to pay poor old Chris a visit.

Sadly, all the ostrich farms have gone now. In some ways I am glad, as I always felt for them in the cold midwinter. With their thin stick like legs, they must have been very cold. They never showed it though; hardy as goats those lads. However, I do miss their mischievousness. They are such inquisitive creatures, always into everything, always eating something. In the many post mortems I have had to carry out on them, I have removed a large number of wonderful things, from pennies, to rubber balls, to bras! All these foreign bodies seem to do little harm to them, but get slowly ground down in their gizzard. Tough as they are, though, I can imagine there's many a concrete motorway flyover in Italy containing a stack of ostriches who fell foul of the mob.

The summer moved on, and the BBC looked harder and harder for more weird and wonderful stories for their programmes. I had been with them to see lame sheep, cows that needed pregnancy work, ostriches and, of course, the Zoo. But none of all the weird and wonderful things that I do in my job had quite prepared me for one consultation that had been fixed up for me by the Beeb.

I had just returned from a morning out on visits when I looked up to see Angela pulling into the car park. She bred cavalier King Charles spaniels and had a particularly friendly stud dog called Brett. He was ageing and soon would have to be retired from active service. In fact, she and I had been discussing just this a few weeks earlier so I wasn't surprised to see her. Unsure of what she wanted, I went down to the waiting room.

Now one of the more delicate jobs that vets have to do occasionally is collect sperm samples from animals. It's the most embarrassing task ever. I think I'd rather dress up in pink hot pants and wander round the night clubs of Mykanos, quite frankly. (Clare made me do that once; ghastly.)

Although we had been trained to do this at the Royal Veterinary College with beagles, they were so used to it that the 'job in hand' was always done easily. Yes, you have to literally manipulate the animal's member. Thankfully, it's not something you're asked to do every day, and I had managed to avoid it for 20 years. Then Angela arrived. Thank you, Angela. Thank you, BBC!!

She asked me to obtain a sperm sample from Brett for analysis to determine his potency. Now, as I've said, it's an embarrassing job at the best of times, so imagine attempting it with a BBC film crew looking over your shoulder. I could well remember the problems I had had talking about rams testicles back in Chester. This was going to call for clever conversations, and subtle photography.

Obviously this wasn't the kind of image the BBC audience wants to see at lunchtime, so we positioned a nurse between the dog and the camera to spare blushes all round. Five minutes later and there was no sperm sample and I could feel myself getting more and more embarrassed and anxious. As for the dog, he may as well have been reading a mag from the waiting room for all he cared. I could hear the occasional chuckle from the crew and nurses. The cameraman was getting tired of this shot and moved around the room to find a different one. That's when the lot of them burst into fits of laughter. You see, they were now positioned so they could no longer see the dog. Just me and my one moving arm, and a grinning nurse standing in front of me. The attempt was abandoned because of hysterics, none of which, I must say, were mine. I've told my staff, the next time a client brings a pet in for a sperm sample, I'll be elsewhere. Unsurprisingly, they never used that footage, much to both Brett's relief and mine. Brett went on to retire and live out a happy life.

The BBC decided to expand their net and include Clare at her racehorse practice. Clare had been treating a horse that was due to go down to Ascot for the big race, and they thought this would be fun to film. Somehow, Clare really has the gift of the gab. When they met to discuss this, Clare managed to persuade them that not only should they film her treating the horse, but also take Clare and Trude down to Ascot for the day to watch the racing. As the final icing on the cake, they'd need lovely new hats because it was ladies' day. The Beeb agreed to pay for it all! I didn't get a new hat so I'm with you in indignantly shouting, "So that's where our bloody licence fee goes is it?"

That said, I had my fun as well. The BBC needed endings for the programmes that involved filming in some wonderful places. On one trip I took Trude and Charlie (our second son) up to Dalby Forest to watch badgers. To add more magic to the film, we went on the Pickering railway line, pretending it was on our way there. Particularly memorable on this great train journey was a game of I Spy, played between Charlie and Trude.

No-one ever beats Charlie, not even when he was the tender age of six. When he asked her if she would like a game, I nearly advised her against it, but thought it would be fun to watch. The BBC thought this would be nice to film, and she accepted. Of course Charlie went first.

"I spy with my little eye, something beginning with T."

Well. Trude went through all the normal Ts. Trees, telegraph poles, tractors, etc., etc. and, after a tortuous mental half-hour, surrendered. The camera crew had long stopped filming and were desperately trying to help crack Charlie's word.

"We give up," they all said finally, surrendering.

"Pigeon," said Charlie, with a triumphant grin, "I win!! My go again." And off he went again. Presumably he meant 'that pigeon' but now you see why he never loses.

I think that the arrival of the train at the station, followed by the evening spent in silence watching the bumbling antics of wild badgers, was a relief to those that had never really met my son. But I'm a proud dad, he had got one over the BBC.

The BBC also decided they wanted some particularly good-quality shots for the start and the end of each show from the Zoo, ideally of the penguins. I didn't see this as being a problem, but I had forgotten I was dealing with the BBC. On the day of filming, not just one van arrived, but three. They planned to lay rail track down so that they could get smooth moving footage of the penguins.

No chance, was my opinion, but, hey, who am I, and what did I know. They carried all their material down to the penguin pond and began to lay out railway track with scientific precision so that it was exactly horizontal. The penguins watched with initial amusement, followed by greater and greater concern, particularly as ever larger cameras arrived and were placed onto the track. By now the penguins were not having any of it. They disappeared into the pool, whizzing around at high speed and, quite rightly in my opinion, stayed there.

"Right, we're ready," said the producer to the keeper.

The keeper grinned, and replied, "For what?"

"Penguins. We need them walking along here."

"You'll have a long wait. They won't come out for hours. Probably when you lot have gone, to be honest."

After an hour, the Beeb accepted that maybe we were right and, shuffling slightly, asked where else they might be able to film.

There was only one set of animals that I could think of that wouldn't mind being filmed, and that was Peter's birds. These parrots are all so well socialised and tame that they are used in the parrot show. They are so used to people and crowds being loud and doing crazy things, that the building of railways wouldn't impress them at all. Practically all the opening sequences of *Vets In The Country* featured parrots.

The BBC was with us from May until September that year. They took over our lives and invaded everything we did. When they finally left, you could almost feel a collective sigh of relief from the surrounding countryside. We had all survived. Truth be known, it was damn good fun, but never again. Not with that number of cameras; I'll leave that to the real TV people.

Besides, Clare and I had other things to think about, in particular a new little critter that entered the world. Our fourth child, Tiger.

Chapter Fifteen

A long time ago, when I first came up to Yorkshire, I was once asked to give a talk to a local parrot society. I was keen to impress with my knowledge on the subject, so sat down and studied parrots in great detail. The fear of the unknown is so often worse than reality itself, and not knowing how knowledgeable they would be was a worry. As I studied, I began to wish the talk had been about insects instead, as I had a ready-made gag/ice-breaker about swatting hard on flies, though, to be fair, I knew little about insects at that time. But it wasn't about insects; it was about parrots, so I couldn't even crowbar the gag in.

A gag is a great last resort if you ever get lost or stuck in a speech, but I made a mental note not to crack the ancient joke about why there aren't any aspirins in the jungle; the answer being that the parrots ate 'em all. The audience, being keen parrot enthusiasts, would have heard it a million times.

I spent a lot of time reading around the subject, trying to ensure that I had as much up-to-date information as I could. It was before the days of laptops and floppy disks, so I had to write all of the talk on acetates. These were thin sheets of plastic that you put onto the projector; your writing was then projected up onto the wall.

The first trick was learning how to master writing on these wretched sheets. No matter how neatly I thought I wrote, when it was projected it seemed to turn into a scrawl resembling another language. Still, this may have some advantages, if they couldn't follow my talk.

Finally the great day came. My talk was in the evening, above one of the many public houses in Pickering. My colleague Andrew said he would like to come along, and I managed to persuade him to drive, so that I could drink. At the end of evening surgery, I climbed into his car, armed with a pile of thin plastic sheets, all carefully separated with tissue paper, and we headed off for Pickering.

We had been working together for about six months now, and my interest in exotic animals was growing, as was the clientele that had the weird and wonderful animals that we looked after. One of these was Howard. He was a large bellicose man, with a ready smile and a great sense of humour. When he wasn't busy running the local pet shop he was a professional chef. He was one of those men who seemed to have unfathomable depths of knowledge when it came to rearing parrots.

He also organised the local parrot society. When we got to the pub, Howard asked me what I would like to drink and, pleased with myself that I was not driving, I ordered a pint of Tetley's. I climbed the thin rickety staircase up to the meeting room, clutching my sheets of plastic and desperately trying not to spill beer all over them. The room was quaint, ideal for cosy fireside meetings or even intimate dinners. I quickly realised that the Tudor beams running down the walls would not help the ability of my audience to read my overheads.

Still, I was not to be discouraged. I put my notes down and, turning round, discovered that the others had returned downstairs. So, draining my pint, I headed back to the bar and joined them all for another pint. After all, we were early, and the beer was good. Twenty minutes later we all ambled back upstairs for 'the vet's talk'. By this stage I was keen to hear what he had to say, until I remembered it was me giving the talk.

I aimed to speak for 40 minutes about parrots and how veterinary science was endeavouring to make huge leaps in the care of the species. Around that time, the only drug that anyone really used when treating parrots was an antibiotic called Terramycin powder; there really wasn't much else to try! It had an OK hit rate, but acted as an immune stimulant that often meant a bird could suddenly perk up and look 'chirpy chirpy cheep cheep' and then drop down dead.

As a result most aviarists (birdkeepers), had a pretty low opinion of vets, so I titled my talk 'There's life after Terramycin powder'. This helped me win over the crowd of 20 hardened Yorkshire men straight away. There were very few vets who specialised in birds, and I think they found it refreshing to finally have someone who had moved into the area who was at least interested.

It went well, and I think they liked me, up to a point. However, the room was hot and stuffy. As the evening progressed, it seemed to get ever hotter and stuffier. As Andrew was driving, when Howard proffered another pint, I accepted. I began to feel quite confident, and warmed more and more to my subject. After all, even before I had spent the weeks revising, I did know my subject fairly well.

Once I had finished talking, I sank gratefully to my seat, took a long last pull on my pint, draining it, and looked for

Andrew so that we could go home. He was deeply engrossed in conversation at the back of the room, and ignoring me completely. At least he wasn't asleep; I took that as a good sign.

Howard stood up and said that there would be a short interval followed by question and answers. I wasn't really ready for there to be a 'questions and answers' session afterwards. I hadn't thought of that.

Howard clambered back up the stairs and passed me another pint. I stared at the pint, and began to feel a bit sleepy. The adrenalin was fast seeping out of my system, and I was ready now for my fireside and slippers. But no.

I fielded a couple of easy questions such as 'what's your favourite type of parrot?' and 'what's the rudest thing you've ever heard a parrot say?' We moved on to more technical problems about diseases and housing. This was fine, but getting harder. The beer, the hot atmosphere and loss of adrenalin were all beginning to have a soporific effect.

"Last question then," said Howard, and pointed towards the back of the room.

A very serious and determined-looking man in the back row stood up and asked me a question about zebras and mules. To this day, I cannot remember exactly what the question was really about, but roughly it was to do with the problems of cross-breeding and genetics. He had been talking to Andrew for a while; Andrew wasn't sure he knew the answer, but knew I would.

I was thrown. Totally! I thought we were there to talk about parrots! In my now-befuddled mind all I could see was visions of zebras running round the Zoo whilst I desperately tried to dart them. But where did the mules come into it? The Zoo didn't have any mules, I thought. And how did this link in to genetics?

I shook my head. Try as I might, I just couldn't shake the image of the Zoo out of my mind. The beer, heat and lack of air had finally won.

I sighed, realising that my evening of hard work was about to come crashing down around my ears as I made a complete idiot of myself. There was an uneasy silence. I swallowed and thought hard. Honesty, however, has always been the best policy in my book.

"I don't know, I'm afraid," I replied. The audience went even quieter; I took another deep breath and said, "Why aren't there any aspirins in the jungle?"

The joke dug me out of a hole and the evening ended on a light note. Actually they roared with laughter, which I assume meant they had had as much to drink as me. As Andrew drove me back to Malton, we discussed the evening.

"Poor joke," he said, "shame you didn't have a better one."

"True," I replied, "but the insect joke was worse."

I went to bed in a haze of zebras chasing mules with parrots stuck on their backs. In the morning over coffee, it suddenly dawned on me that zebras were, of course, types of finches, and mules were hybrids ... Ah it was all so clear now, if only my head was.

Many of the people since have become good clients and even better friends, although I am not sure that I ever saw the breeder of zebra finches again. The event made me realise several things. First, that you should never drink before public speaking, it will always trip you up. This is a good rule, and one that I have stuck to ever since. Second, the well-prepared speech is, on the whole, the easy bit; it is the questions afterwards that are the hard bit. These one can never prepare for. No matter how well one knows one's subject, there will always be one question that puts one onto thin ice.

Since then I have done many talks to societies and social clubs. Many of them just want to hear a few stories about veterinary, and I think it good to tell people how the profession has moved on over the last few decades. Occasionally I talk to the more in-depth societies, and for these I will now spend hours preparing my notes, and I take them very seriously. Fortunately I have yet to be tripped up in such an embarrassing way as I was that first time all those years ago.

Soon after finishing filming *Vets In The Country*, I received one of the more unusual, and yet flattering, phone calls that I have ever received. *Vets To The Rescue* had gone out on BBC1 and *Vets In The Country* was just being aired. The first series of *Zoo Vet* had just been released as a new, longer version. These had all gone done very well. Then I received a phone call from a lady called Avril.

"Is that the vet?" The opening line to most of our phone calls.

"Yes, Matthew Brash speaking," I replied.

"Well, I'm coming to see you," said this voice, "You need an agent, and I have decided that I am going to be it."

She had a sharp, piercing voice with a thick, Huddersfield accent. In fact it was so thick, I wasn't sure that I really understood what she was talking about. But she sounded very interesting, and after talking to her for a while I discovered she was called Avril Barton, had parrots, and didn't live far away. So, if nothing else, we could talk parrots for a while. She came to our home the following week for tea.

Avril didn't drive and so had arranged for a friend called Mark to bring her. Mark ran an after-dinner speaking company, with his father, and he had come along to see if I would be any good at speaking. I had, like all vets, done many talks. But there is a subtle difference between giving talks to the local WI for free, or for a small remuneration towards charity, and being paid large amounts of money to give a talk after a dinner.

Mark chatted to me for a while, and then declared I would make an excellent after-dinner speaker. Well, if he thought so, who was I to disagree? He took my details, told me he was going to put me up on his web site, and he would let me know if anyone wanted to listen to what I had to say.

I didn't entirely understand why I wanted an agent, or even what an agent did, but Avril was fun and determined to become my agent. She was a large lady, enormous in fact, and I felt it probably best not to argue. As we chatted about this and that, I asked her who else she was an agent for.

"Loads of people darling, loads of people, mainly working in the clubs and bars in Leeds."

Aha, I thought singers and comedians, etc.

Avril chatted about the filming; she was keen to be involved in any negotiating. She began to draw up plans as to how I would be a big hit in London or, even better in the States. I admitted that there was to be another series, and she was delighted. I am not sure at what point I ever actually agreed she should be my agent. I think it was just kind of assumed. She would do all the negotiating for me from now on, though what negotiating I was unsure. After tea, we went for a wander round the garden, and she was at the same time amazed and horrified. We had a large, pretty garden, with our big veg patch at the top. She, I don't think, had ever believed that anyone could have such a large garden. She was even more horrified that I actually looked after all this garden.

"What about our hands darling?" she said, worrying. "No more gardening for you, you must look after yourself, you're talent, you are."

So we were talent now, we should look after ourselves, and rest between filming, and not get our hands dirty in the mud. I wasn't entirely sure this was going to work.

But Avril became my agent. She was a great character, sadly no more of this world. She would ring regularly to see how I was, and plan greater and greater things that I should do when we really hit the big time. In time, I began to realise who all her other stars were; perhaps they were not just singers and comedians. It finally hit home when she paid her last visit to me.

Avril rang, and announced she was coming out to the countryside for the day to see me. I invited her and, as she was unable to drive, one of her girls to lunch.

She arrived, chauffeured by Tiffany.

"One of me girls, one of my best girls, love," Avril told me, with a large grin.

Tiffany was a vision of the wonders of modern-day surgery; mainly plastic and silicone. I was impressed. Clare leant over and advised me to shut my mouth as I was beginning to dribble. I had finally clicked that Avril, my agent, was an agent for: one vet, and lots of strippers and ladies of the night. Later I was told she was in fact Leeds' principal Madame. I felt that this had to have a certain amount of kudos. Later in the conversation, when I thought Clare wasn't listening, I asked Avril if she ever had a staff Christmas party. Sadly, Clare had overheard me. There was little or no chance that I would be going, despite Tiffany's entreaties about how much fun they were!! Ah well.

Over lunch, I asked Tiffany whether she was enjoying her trip out into the countryside, and whether she had ever been out this way before.

"Oh yes ducks, come out here all the time. Have to keep the farmers serviced don't we?" leapt in Avril with a reply. And she reeled off a list of farms they visited; many of whom were or had been clients! I decided that our family lived in a much closeted little world.

With Mark setting me up as an after-dinner speaker, I decided I should prepare. I bought a small filing box that could take small envelope-sized cards. On each of these cards I wrote the title of a funny veterinary story. I would then lie there at night rehearsing these stories, until I had them word perfect. Occasionally in the middle of the night, a new story would pop into my head, and I would leap out of bed and rush downstairs to write it down on a card before I forgot it.

This was madness, so I took to having the cards up beside my bed. This meant that all I had to do was reach over, switch on my light and write my new story. Clare couldn't see the advantages, however, finding this rather disturbing. Fortunately, after a couple of nights, I dried up and could think of no new stories.

A few weeks later, Mark rang to say that he had found my first venue for me to start my after-dinner speaking career. Much excitement in the Brash family. It was a lunch party for business people, and they wanted to hear some tall tales from a country vet. This I could manage, I thought. It would be easy enough, and stories of close encounters with fierce creatures soon made the 40 minutes pass quickly.

The next talk, a month later, was harder. An after-dinner talk to a rugby club. I told Mark that I really wasn't sure this was my kind of thing, but he replied that it would be fine; it was, after all, a lunchtime affair. Well lunchtime or no, my recollection of rugby lunches was that they were far from staid affairs. It occurred to me, as I drove to my venue, that they would probably be far happier with Tiffany than me. However, I got a good reception, told some tales of veterinary, and quickly moved on to stories about playing rugby for the Royal Veterinary College. These amused them and, with immense relief, it was soon over, and I headed back home.

I was ready to call it a day, I didn't think this was much fun. You obviously need to be a very special kind of person to be able to give these talks, and I didn't think I had it. So when Mark rang to see of I would give another talk, I said I didn't think so.

"Garstang Country Women's Association," he said. This bunch sounded pretty innocuous; blue rinse, conservative ladies in their 70s. Right up my street. Really, I thought, I ought to be able to do it.

'Garstang Country Women's Association.' Even today the very name sends a cold shiver down my spine. Garstang Country Women's Association ... It'll be fine, I said to myself as I drove over; probably 50 people at most. They had asked me to be there for about seven o'clock so, I figured, as they would all be old ladies, they would probably have had their tea already. I could walk out and talk about the joys of being a country vet for half an hour, and with luck I would be home by 11 p.m. Easy life!!

So I rolled up at a quarter to seven, to be met by the man in reception who said:

"Ah, excellent, you're our after-dinner speaker, aren't you?"

"Yes," I said, gleefully.

"Right, well you're on at 10:30."

Ten thirty, I thought, golly, that's a late, long tea; I do hope the old dears will all still be awake.

"How many people?"

"Oh, 300, 350. You'll be followed by the comedienne."

Slowly the horror of what I had let myself in for began to dawn on me, as I looked round the corner. There, around the bar, several hundred, very drunk, young ladies, from 20 to 40 years old, stood, swaying. It was only ten to seven and they were already beginning to sing. What on earth was I going to stand up and say to keep these girls entertained? This was not what I had trained to do. I felt I would rather face a lion than this lot.

I was about ready to turn and flee, making spurious arguments about an emergency, or tummy bug, anything, when a large arm landed around my shoulder, and I was squeezed in a bear hug.

"Hullo darling," came a voice. Oh God, it's Avril, I thought. But it wasn't, just someone just as large.

"We are the comediennes. Let's go and sit down."

I was whisked off my feet, and manhandled to our table. It was a top table, right bang in the middle of the gigantic dining room, and there was no escape from here. The occupants of most of the tables were beginning to sit down, and the small bread rolls put out in the wicker baskets were beginning to wing their way across the room as a food fight broke out.

The two large ladies, the comedienne and her friend who drove, were sat strategically on either side of me, and grinned. This was their sort of evening.

I think the supper was the worst. As it progressed, it felt like the condemned man's last meal. My advice, if condemned, is don't be too picky about what you have to eat; you really won't taste a thing. My appetite shrank more and more as time passed, and I wished I wasn't driving so I could drink. The comedienne and her friend vainly tried to prop up my wilting self-defences by suggesting veterinary jokes that I might be able to say. When they told them to me, they were funny, I could see that; but a few minutes after telling me, I had already forgotten the punch line. I have never been able to remember jokes, not even as well as my kids. The only suggestion I could come up with was perhaps they should do the veterinary speech as well as the comedienne bit.

Finally dinner ended, the singing settled a bit and, once all the guests had recharged their glasses, they sat back in expectation of riotous veterinary tales. I bravely stood up and spoke for 20 minutes. Silence met my first interesting story. This was one of my best. It almost always got the WI warmed up, but was met by a stony silence from this crowd. This was getting worse and worse. Then an idea occurred to me, I could tell them about testicles. I knew a lot about testicles. Well, that was it. For the last five minutes I managed to whiz through a few ball stories, about rams and llamas and so on. I ended it all with the well-known fact that the veterinary profession is becoming more and more popular with women, for one main reason; it gives women an excuse to castrate anything they like. Well, with this rather weak joke, feeling rather like a wilted flower, I sat down to listen to the comedienne. There was a polite pause, a few claps, and silence. I shrank, but at least I hadn't been lynched.

At this point the comedienne stood up, hitched up her ample breasts and said five very rude swear words in a row. Three hundred people roared with laughter. Presumably with relief that the rather boring vet had finally stopped, as much as at the humour of five swear words.

Even I roared with laughter, just to show that I was one of the gang. After all, my bit was done, and now I could listen to these great witty stories, and enjoy the rest of the evening. You can't beat a good after-dinner speaker.

"Just testing the water, ducks," she said, "just testing the water!!"

Upon which, she turned, looked at me once, smiled, and turned back to her audience. She then proceeded to destroy me in front of 300 drunken women, repeating anecdote after anecdote based on rather weak effeminate men and, in particular, on vets.

I survived, but only just.

At the end, I slunk out to my car avoiding everybody. I dived into it, and drove home in shock. The comedienne had been good, there was no doubt about that, and had she been targeting anyone else, it would have been funny too.

Finally I consoled myself that the ladies had at least had their money's worth; after all, if I hadn't been there then they would never have had me to taunt. It was all character-building stuff, I was sure, but I was equally sure that this was the end of my after-dinner speaking career.

On getting home, I related my tale of woe to Clare, and swore I would never do another after-dinner speech again.

"Well, that's a relief," was Clare's response to it all. "The boys will enjoy having you home to dinner on those extra nights."

I rang Avril the following day, told her what a complete disaster the whole thing had been, and said that I really felt I didn't need an agent, thank you. She understood, she said, and left my life as abruptly as she had entered it. I was surprised by this, expecting some sort of backlash. With hindsight, perhaps she was relieved, as I was never showing as much enthusiasm for the high life as I should. I had continued to dig in the garden, and this had been a constant source of worry to her. I was just a vet who did a bit of filming; there really was no need for an agent.

With my after-dinner speaking career over, I could stop worrying about having to create funny tales. That weekend I ceremoniously burnt my small filing index of witty tales. The bonfire was cathartic and cleansing. I could put it all behind me, and never again go to Garstang Country Club.

Chapter Sixteen

As I write I have just had a rather strong gut feeling that perhaps the deadline given by the publishers is a bit tight!! I have been writing while on duty, initially thinking that a book was only 20,000 words long. However, I have now discovered it is meant to be nearer 80,000 words, and I have a long, long way to go. I have also discovered that if I spend much more than an hour at the computer, I become completely goggle-eyed. Thank god I will never have to be a proper writer, and write a real book!!

When ITV commissioned another series of *Zoo Vet*, it was apparent we would have to rethink how it was done. So Ali Rashid, the owner of Real Life Media Productions, came to see me for the first time. Another 10 of the half-hour episodes had been commissioned, but the filming schedule was going to be tight. We would only have three months to get the whole series in the can. Up until now, filming at the Zoo had gone smoothly, but only on Wednesdays, once a fortnight. What Katie did in the two weeks between each visit I never knew; presumably she filmed for lots of other programmes as well.

With 10 episodes to be filmed in such a short period of time, we would have to film outside the Zoo as well. This would mean filming at the surgery and at home. It was going to be like filming with the BBC again. I agreed, but insisted that it still stayed as just one camera person, and just Katie. Ali agreed, and so *Zoo Vet At Large* was created.

To get sufficient material, lots of filming would have to take place at work. This was going to affect my colleagues, and they would need a bit of persuading after the BBC. However, they are a great bunch and, with only a bit of arm twisting, they agreed and filming got underway. Diana had already done a lot of filming and so she was the logical choice to use as much as possible. She was relaxed in front of the camera, and able to concentrate on her job as nurse without being distracted.

Although I now had the cameras with me for a lot of the time, somehow they were never there when I really wanted them. Murphy's Law, I guess. An example of this was when I had to visit the gilamonsters.

They tell me a vet should remain calm and professional at all times, and I always do. Well nearly. Apart from when I visit 'Gilamonster House'.

This was a client of mine's home in which he had installed many tanks and vivaria to house his somewhat substantial collection of reptiles. Some of these were gilamonsters, a rare kind of Mexican lizard that's as breathtaking to look at as it is dangerous. It is a foot long, robustly built, with either red and black, or yellow and black, stripes. It's classed as a dangerous animal because its venom is potentially fatal. Owners are required by law to keep specially formulated anti-venom for emergencies. And, by law, I had to inspect the collection annually, which I didn't have a problem with. It was his 'street of snakes' that gave me the creeps. Don't get me wrong, I love snakes, it's just the way he'd set them out. In one large room, he had rows and rows of open-fronted snake tanks stacked one on top of each other. These ran down the sides of the room, facing one another, with just enough room to walk in between them. It felt eerie, walking slowly down the street of snakes. They were never happy that I was in their territory, and would rear up and hiss at me, one every foot or so, as I passed them by. Not only that, they'd lunge forward trying to strike. The subdued lighting and dank odour added to my overwhelming sense of fear. I often used to wonder if I would ever get out of there alive. Actually you know, if Hannibal Lecter had had a house in England, then this would have been it.

The client would always invite me to have a look at the snakes, and on one occasion I rang my nurse and asked her to ring my mobile in 10 minutes time. If I timed it right, I could inspect the gilamonsters, take the call, and be out of there before he asked me to visit the street of snakes. If I didn't answer, then the nurse was to call the police.

The inspection went well, but after 10 minutes there was no call. I tried to make it drag on a while longer, but there was still no call 15 minutes later. She'd obviously forgotten. I finished the inspection and he asked me whether I wanted to see how the snakes were doing. Marvellous, I thought, and in I went. Five minutes later I was out of there and driving back to the clinic when the mobile went. It was my nurse.

"You did say 20 minutes didn't you, Matt?" she asked.

I was tempted to wish her good luck at the Job Centre, but I decided I would just ask her to come with me next time I visited that particular client. She could take a stroll down the street of snakes, while I inspected the gilamonsters. Of course, I cursed to myself, where was the camera when I needed it!

The cameras were not there in the night either, and this meant that they often missed some of our more unusual and sometimes unbelievable work. A client of mine rang me in the wee small hours saying his dog, Moss, had keeled over. I was in bed! He was hysterical about it, and sounded a little worse for drink.

I tried to get him to bring the dog to the surgery, and I'd meet him there. Home visits, particularly emergencies, are difficult if you haven't got the right equipment and drugs with you. The time lost in having to go to someone's home, then collect the animal yourself, and take it into the surgery for treatment, can mean lost minutes that could be crucial. He was adamant, however, that I should come to him, and finally admitted he'd been drinking. Like I needed him to tell me, the vapours were coming down the phone! So I succumbed and leapt in the car en route for his house.

Once there, I saw he'd been drinking whisky; nothing wrong there, but I was deeply concerned at Moss's appearance. He was flat out, panting with his tongue hanging out. The dog wouldn't have looked out of place slumped over a bar in a seedy pub. My client assured me that this wasn't what it looked like, he hadn't given the dog booze, and upon checking I found this to be true. His eyes were flicking from side to side, the classic symptoms of a stroke. A small blood vessel had burst, upsetting his ability to balance. Unable to stand without falling over, he had then collapsed. Not understanding why he couldn't see straight, let alone stand, Moss was stressed, and the exaggerated concerns of his owner weren't helping. I gave him some injections to help counteract the effects of the stroke. There was little we could do for the burst blood vessel, but if we could keep the dog quiet and calm, then this would allow the bleeding to stop and speed up recuperation. Many dogs can do very well after strokes, provided we manage the anxiety. What Moss needed more than anything else was a calm, collected owner. I spent some time explaining this, and assured the owner that Moss should all be right. What Moss needed was peace and quiet to sleep it all off. I also offered the owner the same advice. He took the advice, and in the morning he rather groggily rang me back and said the dog was much better but still unable to walk in a straight line. A picture sprang to mind of them both sat in the living room with ice packs on their heads and nursing glasses of Alka-Seltzer.

Sadly, a month later the same client rang back, this time sober, to tell me the dog had had a relapse. I went along to his house and poor old Moss was ready for the old 'street of lampposts and slow-running postmen in the sky'. I administered the injection and he passed away peacefully. We took him out to the garden and I helped bury him. At least his suffering was over. I told the owner to have a drink and toast his old chum, and he did just that.

However, I thought he might have hit the bottle a little too hard, as the next day I got yet another phone call from him saying that his pet was back!

"Impossible," I said, "he was dead." I had checked him thoroughly.

"If you don't believe me, then you had better come and have a look."

As I raced over there, my mind was reeling with what could have gone wrong, the dog clawing its way back from the grave, and a ruddy big lawsuit. When I got there I was a little taken aback. The owner believed that the dog had returned ... as a cat. Apparently he had woken, looked out of the window at the still-fresh grave, and there, sitting on it, was a cat with the exact same black and white markings that the dog had had. True enough, the markings were strikingly similar! Was it life after death? You've got to admit it was odd. How come its fur was the same colours? How come it was perched patiently on the grave of the dog? It'd certainly never been seen in the area before, and no one had lost such a feline. It makes you think. If there is such a thing as reincarnation, then I wonder if you get a choice. If so, I'm coming back as Nicole Kidman's husband. Mind you, knowing my luck, I'll probably come back as Nelson the chimp's wife.

Although we film for a lot of the year, it is always rather tragic that the camera just isn't there when you really want it.

Chapter Seventeen

I always seem to have had a funny relationship with bears. My first dealings with them were within my first few weeks of starting at The Mount Vet Group back in 1991. I had already been out to the Zoo the week before, when Neville rang to say that Winnie, the old North American brown bear, was limping badly. Excited, and still feeling very nervous about the whole zoo vet thing, I jumped into my car and raced out to the Zoo as fast as I could.

Neville greeted me, and explained that Winnie was an old brown bear nearing her 50s. She occasionally had a bit of a limp in the winter, but she had jumped off a rock and was now limping badly. She was obviously very unhappy with her back left leg. There was no blood to be seen, so a cut or wound was unlikely. It was looking serious, and may even have been broken.

"The bear will need to be anaesthetised," I said, "so I can get a closer look."

"Will she be alright under the anaesthetic? She's pretty old," came the gruff reply.

This was one of those telling moments, I think. Would the bear be alright? Well I hoped so, but, as Neville had so pointedly told me, she was pretty old. With any animal an anaesthetic is a risk, but this obviously increases as they get older. With normal pets, we are able to minimise these risks with pre-operative blood tests to ensure they are able to withstand the rigors of an anaesthetic, but this would not be possible with Winnie. However, she was not able to walk on her leg at all, so we would need to do something, that was for sure.

"I don't think I've much option," I said, "we can't simply do nothing, and if it is broken then we will really need to think about putting her to sleep."

This was not going well. I had only been the Zoo's vet for a minute, and already I was thinking of putting their much-loved bear to sleep.

"Alright," replied Neville, "you're the vet."

Winnie was a glutton for food, so it was easy to tempt her inside into her den. She didn't weigh much, compared with the larger polar bears, so only a small amount of anaesthetic was needed. This would fit nicely into just the one dart. I dropped the dose down even more, seeing as she was so old, and fired a dart into her.

She was quickly fast asleep and, after the normal routine of prodding and poking, we went in. She was well out. I bent down to examine the leg, and got my first whiff of bear. By God they smell; they really, really whiff! This is nothing to do with being kept in captivity, but more to do with personal hygiene. Mind you, in fairness, it can't be easy to keep yourself clean when you have a three-inch thick fur coat. Overcoming my nauseous feelings, and starting at the top, I felt my way slowly down the limb. I began to get a feeling of the majesty of such a great animal. This was a body that normally carried a lot of power, but under the thick, brown fur that made the leg look sturdy, there was just a skinny little leg. She had been losing weight for a while from not putting all her mass on her leg when she walked. This is known as disuse atrophy, and works on the principal that if you don't use it, you lose it. There was no obvious break, but when I finally reached the ankle joint it was crunchy as I manipulated the bones up and down.

"She's got bad arthritis, I think, but I can't be sure whether she has actually broken it or not. I am going to need to X-ray it. Do you think we can take her back to the surgery for me to X-ray?"

Neville looked at me, and then the bear, in sheer astonishment.

"You're joking, aren't you?" he said.

I realised at this point that perhaps this wasn't a very common thing to do.

I told him I was serious, and assured him the bear was flat out and I had more anaesthetic on hand should I need any. It was simply the best way to get a decent look at her joints and see just how bad the problem really was. I could also clean up her teeth as well.

"Alright," said Neville, "you're the vet."

This, I soon discovered, is a common expression that people use when they don't really agree with what you're about to do. It'll probably, one day, be on my gravestone: 'Matt Brash - well, he was the vet!'

We loaded Winnie easily into a small cage in the back of the Zoo's van and, with me leading the way, we drove back to the surgery. Once there, we quickly unloaded her. She was still fast asleep, and so I was able to slip a tube down her throat and connect her up to gaseous anaesthetic. We would now be able to keep her asleep for as long as we needed.

I asked the nurses to X-ray her and popped out to have a word with Neville. There I bumped into my new boss.

"How did you get on with that bear at the Zoo?" he asked.

"No problem," I boasted. I told him about my tentative diagnosis and that I'd decided to X-ray the bear to be sure. He nodded in agreement and asked how I was going to do that, seeing as there was no X-ray facility at the Zoo.

I told him it was all under control and we were busy X-raying the bear on the table at the moment. It was his turn to look at me in astonishment, as though I was mad. He then turned and walked off muttering under his breath, presumably quite rightly cursing the day he'd ever taken me on.

We got some good X-rays and the pock-marked changes on the bone, classic signs of degenerative arthritis, were clearly visible. Of fractures there were no signs.

"Good news," I said to Neville, "she has sprained her ankle and it's made all the worse by her arthritis."

We loaded Winnie back into her crate for the return trip to the Zoo. I gave her some painkillers, and handed Neville a packet of arthritis drugs.

"She will need one of these a day, hidden in a jam sandwich or something," I said proudly. Perhaps I was finally becoming the Zoo vet.

The following week, on my routine visit, we went and checked up on Winnie. She was now much happier than she had been for a long time. It was so satisfying to have diagnosed a problem in such an old animal and successfully treated it. Winnie was climbing up rocks that she hadn't bothered with for a long time. With the increase in exercise that she was getting, she would quickly rebuild the muscles on her limbs. It was a lovely feeling.

Neville then asked me to take a look at one of the ostriches that was limping. Lameness was obviously going to be a feature of zoo veterinary work. The ostriches are a different kettle of fish all together, however, provided one is calm and quiet, they are relatively easy to deal with. The cause of the lameness was easy to diagnose, the large male had cut his foot on a flint. A course of antibiotics and painkillers would do the trick, of that I was confident.

It was an hour later, whilst drinking coffee back at the surgery, that I first began to notice that I was feeling a bit itchy. I had been scratching a bit since I had got back during evening surgery, but now was feeling really tickly. Suddenly the answer crawled across my not unhairy arm. It was a large ostrich louse. Lice on dogs and cats aren't small, but ostrich lice are massive, easily a good half centimetre long. Upon checking my arms I realised that my intimate meeting with the ostriches had left me with a number of companions. Yuk, they're revolting things; the lice, not the ostriches. I leapt up, discarding clothes as I went. As always in these cases, one's imagination begins to run riot, and enormous hordes of blood-sucking lice were now foremost in my mind. They all came out easily enough in the shower, so I didn't really need to worry, but another lesson had been learnt. Zoo animals carry bigger and badder bugs than our domestic friends. I now spend hours treating for these nasty little suckers at any opportunity.

Winnie went on to have a happy last year, and died peacefully in her sleep aged well over 50. A remarkable age for a brown bear, or should that be a grey bear at that age.

The two polar bears, however, were indestructible. They never seemed to ail in any way, and so it was quite a shock when Marcus suddenly passed away a few years later, leaving Mandy on her own. Although his death was natural, from old age, the circumstances were most unusual.

Imagine you love polar bears so much that it borders on obsession. Well, there was a man who lived in London who was like that. He was passionate about bears and, more specifically, about polar bears.

At that time, there were only two zoos in Britain that laid claim to having polar bears, one in Edinburgh, the other Flamingo Land. One day the Zoo received a phone call from a lady who wanted to arrange a special birthday surprise for her fiancé, who was a wildlife fanatic and adored polar bears in particular. She wanted to arrange a lavish treat that involved meeting a polar bear in the flesh. Well, in the fur. Her plan was to travel up from London and stay in a lovely pub in Hovingham, with a five-course evening meal and four-poster bed, and then bring him along to meet the bear the following day as a surprise.

It was all arranged, and a few weeks later he came along to the Zoo, blindfolded for extra fun and tension. Ruth met the couple and took the lucky 30-year-old along to meet Mandy and Marcus.

The man was in his element. It was a dream come true, and his excited expression was a picture of delight when the blindfold was removed and he came face to face with two real live polar bears! It was a jolly occasion, and Ruth told him of Marcus' passion for Polo mints and asked the chap if he'd like to give him some. The man passed Marcus a Polo through the bars. Marcus had always been a soft bear, and would lick them delicately off your flat hand. I am sure that he didn't have a malicious bone in his body. He made short work of the first

Polo, and then looked up for another, which he crunched and swallowed.

Then a third, which he sucked and crunched; and then he fell down dead.

Yes, poor old Marcus gave a guttural moan and flopped into a big heap of defunct polar bear. After a stunned silence, the realisation sank in as the man's dream turned into a nightmare. He burst into tears and was utterly inconsolable. He was convinced he had just murdered one of the only three polar bears in Britain.

Ruth called me immediately, and I dashed up to the Zoo. He was stone dead. Moving anything that weighs more than 700 kilos is never easy, and moving dead weight has always been challenging.

It was a Saturday, the Zoo hadn't opened yet, and we needed to get him off show somehow, as exhibiting an ex-bear didn't seem right. As if to add insult to injury, I had to ask the man to help me move the corpse; there was no one else there to help. He was still sobbing, and now he was being asked to move the corpse of the polar bear he thought he'd just murdered.

I tried to console him by saying at least he got the chance to physically handle a polar bear, and not many people get that opportunity, but it didn't help. He was thinking he wouldn't be touching it if he hadn't have killed it. I knew that that was going through his mind; you could tell by the weeping.

Later that day I did a quick post mortem and managed to uncover that the cause of death was kidney failure and not Polo-cide, so he was off the hook. I rang him in London and let him know; he was very relieved. It had been a million to one coincidence that the bear had dropped down dead at that moment. Poor bloke. I really felt for him. Still, one thing was for sure, he wasn't going to forget his 30th in a hurry!

Ruth, of course, never shares her mints with anybody now, but then no one asks for one, either. It may seem flippant, but I can't look at a packet of Polos without thinking of poor Marcus.

Marcus had passed away, leaving Mandy on her own. I was worried about how she would be. They had been together for nearly 30 years and had appeared inseparable. Most of this time had been spent at the Zoo, after they had been rescued from a circus. I rang Edinburgh Zoo and they assured us that their lone polar bear was very happy. After all, they spend most of their time in the wild on their own.

We were criticised for having a single bear but, you know, after Marcus died, she seemed to come into her own. She became livelier and seemed to come out of her shell. Perhaps Marcus had suppressed her for all those years. She was happy, and far too old to rehouse, so we decided to let her live out the rest of her days at the Zoo. She was certainly spoilt by the keepers. To keep her entertained, they used to make her ice-cream lollypops. These aren't your normal run-of-the-mill lollypops, but much larger. They were made in a dustbin. First, six inches of fish would be put into the bottom of the bin and covered with water before being put into a giant freezer. Once frozen, a layer of meat would be added, and so on. Each day another layer of fruit or meat or jam sandwiches would be added, until the bin was full of frozen food in layers. This would then be turned out, and the large, gigantic ice-lolly rolled down to Mandy. As she saw it coming, she would bounce up and down with excitement, just like a kid at Christmas. It would be rolled into the pool, where it would bob and bounce as Mandy tried to break it open. A lolly like this would often keep her entertained for several days. Her other great joy was car tyres with food stuffed inside. A kind of giant rubbery bagel, if you like. These she could twist and turn into amazing shapes, demonstrating the power in her paws. All the different methods of enrichment that we give the animals at the Zoo are designed to help them mimic their natural behaviour as if they were in the wild. It is the constant day-to-day task of the keepers to put something different in everyday.

Chapter Eighteen

This is interesting; I am actually really, really enjoying writing this. It surprises me, because when I was at school I often had to write essays for my English homework. I dreaded it because they were always returned with 'rubbish, not worth even reading' scribbled across the top (usually spelt wrong). This had not done my confidence much good, but then, if you've read this far, maybe I'm not as bad as my old teachers would have had me think.

When Katie stopped working for Real Life Media Productions, I really thought that this would be the end of *Zoo Vet At Large*. I had had a great relationship with her over so many years, and I couldn't see how anyone could replace her. She really was the programme. Although it was me she filmed, it was her photography, her way of putting it all together. All I had to do was be myself and plough on. How hard is that? Apart from which, when you have a job that is as fun as mine, it really is not hard to be enthusiastic. The series had had a good innings, I mused.

So when Ali Rashid rang to say they would like to film another series, I was surprised. Ali knew I had concerns about Katie not being involved, so he came out to see me. A new series had been commissioned and he had found a new producer he thought I would like. She was half Spanish/Basque and, like Katie, a self-employed producer. Ali thought we would get on and he was sending her out to meet me.

So along came Izaskun Arrieta. To be honest, I don't think I've ever managed to say her full name out aloud correctly. Thankfully, upon meeting her she said "Hi, call me Izzie".

Izzie was, and is, because we are still filming at the moment, the most wonderful camera person. Again no crew, no sound guy, no script, no make up, no digital effects and largely no retakes. What you see is what actually happened.

Izzie is such a relaxed person that it made me feel at ease immediately. Unbeknown to me at the time, the real reason she had come to see me was to decide whether she actually wanted to work with this idiotic vet out in the wolds of Yorkshire!!

I suspect that she was born holding a camera, which would have made for a difficult birth but at least they would have had a record of it. If it hadn't been filmed, she would have felt it a missed opportunity.

Izzie decided to take me on, and so we started to film another series of *Zoo Vet At Large*. She and I quickly developed a natural rapport. She encouraged me to talk to the camera, as if I was talking directly to the viewer at home. Our friendship, and her willingness to leap in and ask me questions when I am not explaining myself, has prompted me to talk naturally to camera without, hopefully, blinding viewers with science. Hopefully I don't come over all preachy and condescending either.

Izzie's natural intuition, knowing one end of an animal from t'other, also means she gets her shots straight away, which is a blessing. I have found over years of filming that the animals are even worse actors than I am.

Imagine trying to give stage directions to a cage full of ring-tailed lemurs. Or explaining to a depressed camel what its motivation is. Or telling a newly neutered lion that we didn't really 'believe' how it woke up from the anaesthetic and could it try it again. It's not going to happen, be honest.

I think I'd better stop waxing lyrical about Izzie before you either throw up or decide we are having an affair!

Izzie started filming. She joined me on my fortnightly visits to the Zoo but would also come to the surgery on a daily basis and film any exotic or interesting case that might come in.

So when I received a call from Mr and Mrs Page, I knew Izzie would enjoy filming them. I had met them earlier in the year, when they had only recently moved to their smallholding high up on the Yorkshire moors, near Whitby.

The Pages have a number of rescued small primates taken from bad homes. They have collected them over the years and given them a wonderful and secure environment in which to live and prosper. They are their 'kids', as they call them. Earlier that year, one of the squirrel monkeys had badly broken its arm in an accident. We had fixed it, but whilst it healed the Pages had become regular visitors, and were by now good friends.

The little monkey had been over doing it on the bananas. Yes, I know, monkeys are supposed to eat bananas, I've seen cartoons too; but they need other foods as well to make a well-balanced diet. Monkeys can get addicted to bananas very easily, and bananas are high in phosphorous and this blocks calcium uptake, resulting in weak bones.

When the Pages rang on this particular day, they were very distraught. Bobo had cut his hand badly whilst helping to do the washing up. (Their dishwasher had broken down, so to speak.) They had no chance of getting him down to me, so would I come up to them. It is never ideal visiting animals in their own homes. The animal always seems to have the upper hand before you have even started, but they were desperate so off we went.

We effectively had to pack the operating theatre into the car, if I was going to be able to operate on Bobo there and then. So with all that, and Izzie's camera equipment, it was rather a squeeze.

The drive up over the moors from Pickering to Whitby is so beautiful that actually I was glad of an excuse to go. The heather was in full bloom and the day was quite glorious as we went.

The Pages lived on a quiet little road hidden off the main road, shortly before you get to Whitby. They had bought an old house and had been busy converting it to accommodate their entire menagerie. Out the back they had built a complex of cages for their 'children'.

They could go in with them, feed them, groom them and play with them, trusting the animals implicitly. The cages were connected by a complex of tunnels that ran all over, including from the garden down to the house and into the kitchen. This also allowed the monkeys to come down into the kitchen. There the Pages had constructed a special cage so that the monkeys could watch telly, or even join Mum and Dad for tea when they felt like it.

The house was stuffed with much-loved animals of all descriptions; quite honestly it made our menagerie at home look positively pitiful.

On our arrival, we waded our way past the dogs and the geese, pushed the donkeys to one side and made it to the front door. We were greeted effusively by the Pages, who were up to their armpits in fur as they'd been grooming the dogs. We were led into the kitchen.

There, in the specially constructed cage, was Bobo, sitting looking miserable and watching telly (*Eastenders* probably, he looked *really* miserable).

As I walked over to him, he held out his hand to show me his injury. If he could have talked English, he would no doubt have said, 'See, see what I've done, ouch!'

The wound was sufficiently deep that I could see the tendons. If we were to ensure that he still had the use of his hand, then we would have to stitch it closed.

"It will need some stitches," I said, turning to his worried parents.

They looked a bit alarmed, but had suspected the same themselves. I assured them that we would be using an anaesthetic similar to one a doctor might use on a child. Isoflorane gas is quick and very effective.

I brought all the anaesthetic kit in from the car, whilst the Pages cleared the decks in the kitchen. We cleaned the surface down and turned it into an operating theatre. For years now, I had been using a modified anaesthetic machine that fits nicely into my car. It's ideal for carrying out operations in the field. It had proved its use by being small and manoeuvrable time and time again, and this was no exception,

Once we were all set, Mr Page got Bobo out of his cage. The little monkey sat in Mr Page's arms trustingly, as I placed a face mask over his head. The anaesthetic gas is tasteless and very quick, and within a minute Bobo was fast asleep.

The wound was easy to clean. I removed any infected-looking tissue and then sewed the edges back together. The tricky bit about giving monkeys stitches is that, like children, they pick at them and can easily reopen the wounds. To stop them doing this, we hide the stitches under the skin as well as putting them in the skin. Then, even if they do remove the ones they can see, there is still another layer they cannot see, holding everything together.

As soon as I had put the last stitch in, I turned the anaesthetic gas off so that he could wake up. I gave him painkillers and antibiotics by injection and planned to leave the Pages more antibiotics to give him in a treat over the next few days.

Bobo began to wake up. The Pages' worried looks began to disappear. Bobo sat on the kitchen table with a surprised look on his face, looking round, wondering what on earth had happened.

"Isn't he doing well!" said Mrs Page.

"Isn't he brave!" said Mr Page. "For being such a brave little lad, you can have a lolly."

Mr Page reached over to a shelf behind and lifted off a jar full of lollies. He offered the jar to Bobo. This was obviously a common treat. Bobo chose his favourite, a red one, and expertly unwrapped it and began to lick it. Izzie filmed with a small, happy smile on her face. I watched in absolute amazement; now I had seen everything. If I'd had my digital camera on me, I would have snapped a picture and sent it to a greeting card company. This little monkey was an absolute star. Bobo's a lucky kid to have such wonderful adopted parents.

As Izzie and I climbed back into the car and drove back to Stamford Bridge, we were both silent. We both felt that we had just witnessed something quite remarkable. The sheer intelligence of the little monkey, and the obvious deep bond that existed between him and his parents. I think we all got a little treat that day, not just Bobo.

Sadly, not all my clients are quite that animal wise, and even with hindsight I have never known whether it was a blessing or a curse that Izzie was not there the day the Burtons came.

Let me explain. I always maintain that a basic knowledge of the pet you want to buy is important. Owning a pet isn't a right, it's an honour and you should always be 100% certain about what you're getting yourself into. Thankfully, most people do investigate the pros and cons of pet ownership. Then there are those who go into it blindly. Then there are the Burtons.

They sounded quite intelligent people when I spoke to them on the phone for the very first time. They admitted to never owning a pet before they succumbed to a sign by the side of a road which read, 'Yello Labrador puppy's for sale.' For the Burtons it was a very bad sign, and I don't just mean because of the poor spelling and grammar. They pulled in and purchased one of the tiny puppies, which they were told was only just over a fortnight old. The Labrador, not much more than a bundle of fluff, instantly became the apple of their eye and they took it to its new home.

The following day they rang. They realised that they should have thought about it all more carefully, but were now ringing to chat about feeding, worming and general care. We offered to have them in for one of our 'puppy health checks' and even to come along to Scallywags, our socialisation classes, but they felt that it was a bit early. Charlie was still very small, but they would come in when he was eight weeks old for his first vaccinations. So I put them through to one of our nurses, who then chatted to them for half an hour about all the things that they would need to know to bring up Charlie healthily.

A month later and they were having suspicions that all was not well with Charlie, so they rang and made an appointment to bring him in. Charlie had barely grown in 4 weeks, and my immediate thoughts turned to congenital abnormalities or dwarfism. Both of which aren't unheard of in dogs. The Burtons were adamant that they were doing everything correctly. They were feeding him properly and had even attempted lead-training, but nothing was working.

Charlie was still a shrimp!

Later that day the whole family arrived in their immaculate people carrier, already done out for Charlie. It had a large dog grill across the back, and a hand-made wooden dog bed filling the boot. Charlie, however, was not caged in the boot, but sitting safely on the back seat between the Burtons' two young sons. He was safely tucked up in a small, cosy shoebox, as befitted his stature.

They carried him into the waiting room, and perched themselves on the edge of their seats as they waited for their turn. I called them through, and they proudly marched in as a clan, ready to show off their pride and joy, Charlie.

As I opened the lid, my mind was still awash with the possible causes of Charlie's growth problems. Then, my keen, highly trained, veterinary eye spotted the reason in a trice.

Charlie was a guinea pig!

Quite a happy little fellow, nice little dog collar and everything, but a guinea pig all the same. I looked up from the box, and looked over to my computer. No, it wasn't April the first!! I turned back to Mr Burton and, whilst trying hard not to giggle, told him the bad news. The Burtons let forth a deafening silence: genuinely stunned.

I turned to the boys to explain.

"Charlie is a guinea pig and not a dog after all," I said.

"Will he be alright mister?"

"He'll be fine," I said.

"Why won't he grow mister?"

I explained to the two that Charlie was a perfectly healthy normal-sized fully grown guinea pig. In fact, he was really a she, and I suspected she may be pregnant. I didn't think they needed to know that just yet. At this point, one of the boys let out a squeak of pleasure.

"Wicked," he said. "I never wanted him to grow any bigger, he wouldn't have fitted in my school bag."

Mr and Mrs Burton looked relieved, as well as somewhat sheepish.

Izzie had missed it, but could we really have filmed them and then shown it on TV? I am not sure I would have really wanted to.

We were soon back at the Zoo. My good old arch enemy, Nelson, was in trouble. When we got there, we found him sat in the corner of his large enclosure looking utterly fed up, but not in pain.

"He's been like that for a few days," said Ruth. "We have given him some antibiotics, and even tried painkillers. He perked up, but there is still something annoying him in there."

He had, what looked like, a stick protruding from his mouth jutting upwards. He spent his time alternating between chewing at it and pulling at it with his fingers. He had to be feeling pretty miserable, as for the first time that I could remember he wasn't shouting the place down or hurling abuse, and anything else he could muster, at me.

"At first we thought some idiot had ignored the 'don't feed the animals' sign again and flicked a lolly stick in which Nelson had picked up, chewed and got jammed in his teeth," continued Ruth.

It is amazing that visitors to the Zoo will still give the animals 'treats'. A few years ago we lost a baby penguin because someone flicked a lolly stick into its food. So please, when you're at a zoo, **bin your rubbish and don't feed the animals.**

With the penguin we had found out too late. On post mortem, we had found a five-inch long lollypop stick stuck in his stomach. The end had rubbed its way through the wall of the stomach, leading to peritonitis. I didn't want to lose Nelson in the same way, but it was not going to be easy.

"We are going to have to knock him out. Then we can have a good look at whatever it is, and remove it if needed. Whilst I have him asleep we'll give the rest of him a 10,000 mile service, clean his teeth, take some bloods, and so on," I said.

We gave him some more painkillers to be going on with, and planned to come back the following day. In the morning we returned. I had brought Diana with me, so that she could look after the anaesthetic whilst I cleaned his teeth and worked on him. As she set up all the gear we needed in the operating theatre, I went to dart him.

As ever, this took an age, but eventually we got him darted and asleep. Now, as I have said before, the scary part of a vet's job is the point where you have to physically go into the knocked-out animal's cage and start work. You have to be 100% sure that they're under. By now, we had given a name to our system of approaching them. It's not a very good acronym, but it was the best we could come up with. The PWAB system. This stands for Poke the bugger With A Broom. Well, to the PWAB there was no reaction and we felt that Nelson was 'chasing bananas and vets in the sky'. As I was happy he was out, I went in and looked in his eyes, and he seemed well asleep.

He was a heavy chimp, probably weighing nearly 70 kilos, so it was going to take three of us to carry him through to the operating theatre. Ruth, the head keeper, and I took a hairy arm each, whilst the curator took Nelson's feet. It was at this point Nelson opened his eyes and looked at us. Utter terror struck all three of us and we dropped him. Well, I thought I was sharp on my feet, but the curator was out of the cage, locking the door behind him, before the chimp hit the ground. Ruth and I froze; Nelson sat up, gave us a blank look, and passed out again. Oh blessed relief! Now, of all the animals in the world, the one I would not like to be locked in a cage with is Nelson. The problem is he is intelligent, and very, very strong. He doesn't like me, he knows who I am, and would just love to get his hands on me. The last chimp that escaped, in Poland, sought out the vet and bit his hands off!! Now if that isn't vindictive, I don't know what is.

He had fallen straight back to sleep, so, in haste, I changed my plan about working on him in the operating theatre and decided to operate on him in his own indoor cage. I would rather have him rampaging in his quarters than around the park. We brought in all the kit. Passing a tube down his throat, we connected him up to the anaesthetic machine. Now we had control!

On closer inspection, we found the offending foreign object wasn't foreign at all but a tooth. It had rotted and then become loose. It was still attached by a small piece of tissue from his gum. It was the simplest of jobs to remove the offending tooth, and give him a full check over. We took bloods and cleaned the rest of his teeth, and gave him a pedicure.

As soon as we had finished, I reversed the anaesthetic and we left him on a thick pile of straw to wake up.

As we left the Zoo, Izzie wasn't the slightest bit phased about my narrow escape.

"That was great," she said, "I got it all on camera! Very exciting!"

I suggested to Ruth we might put the curator in the cage with Nelson to keep him company while we had a long lunch, but she's more forgiving than I am and recommended we just let his car tyres down.

Three years later, Nelson is still going strong, and still doesn't like me!

Chapter Nineteen

The camera now began to enter our home life slightly more than we had allowed it to before. Izzie used to come and join us for breakfast before I went off to the Zoo, and so it was logical in many ways that she would sooner or later end up filming our chaotic mornings. We have a routine, shambolic as it is. All the animals need to be cleaned, fed and watered. Then we have to do the same with the children. It rarely goes according to plan, and Izzie captured a typical Brash morning several times.

Fly had passed away, having reached the grand old age of nearly 16, and even Kipper, now nearly eight, was beginning to feel his age. Sadly Curlew the Burmese cat had also passed away, and been replaced by a new Burmese, Voodoo. Along the way a myriad of other animals had dropped in to enrich our lives. There had been Sharky, the red-tipped shark, Army the mouse, the canaries, and a regular procession of wild animals, all in need of some sort of repair. Most of these animals would come home with me, needing a new home. They would be greeted with open arms, and the children would set to, trying to nurse them back to full recovery. Any deaths were always treated very seriously, and burials would always be with full military honours. The graveyard running up the side of the garden was getting longer, and I had to be careful exactly where I mowed.

Spring would always herald the arrival of enormous quantities of frogspawn. These rapidly developed into frogs and could be found all over the kitchen. The stick insects that had arrived in the post for somebody's birthday had long since had enormous numbers of offspring, and these too had escaped. They had a particular fondness for orchids, so could normally be tracked down on the brave and slowly diminishing orchid plant in the kitchen.

Rosie, the cockatoo, had become an integral part of our lives. She would spend all day out of her cage, helping either Lucinda or Clare with the housework. She chewed anything that came in sight, particularly pens. She had a ready supply of interesting beak fodder, as the four children left all and sundry everywhere. I must say, she was extraordinarily tolerant of the children, allowing them to carry her all over the house, sometimes upside down, sometimes under their jumpers, without so much as removing a chunk o'child.

Rosie made the greatest of additions to the family, so it was with great alarm in her voice that Clare rang one day to say that Rosie had injured herself. She had stupidly walked across the Aga and burnt her leg. There had been no sign of any injury initially, but a few hours later she had started to chew her leg. Cockatoos are notoriously stupid cannibals, and she had now eaten a hole in the back of leg.

Despite two operations, I was unable to sort the problem out. Despite cleaning the wound and suturing the edges closed, despite collars and painkillers, she just chewed it all to pieces. Finally it was all too much. Certainly one of the more difficult telephone calls I have ever had to make was to tell Clare that our Rosie had just died. I knew she was devastated, but for the children it was going to be far worse. But perhaps spending all their time with injured wild animals had hardened the children, as they took it better than we did.

Sometimes it is only when a pet has gone that you realise how much you really enjoyed their company. For this reason I have never been species-ist. Some pets mean a lot more to some people than to others. To a farmer a cat may just be vermin, whilst to others their cat is their sole reason for living. I know for a fact that Tiger, son number four, nearly goes into terminal decline if one of his chickens is poorly.

In fact I regularly get clients bringing much-loved chickens into the surgery. They are the daftest of creatures, but very amusing to watch.

So in some ways it was no surprise when Mr Bosun brought his chicken to the surgery. He had seen the TV programme and had brought his chicken up from Lincolnshire for me to look at. He had been to his local vets, but they didn't think there was anything they could do. Mr Bosun wondered if the vet off the telly would have better luck.

He placed the basket on the table as I asked him what the problem was.

"It's me chicken," he said, "She won't eat, is miserable, and now she has a swollen tummy."

"How many chickens have you got?" I asked.

"Oh about a dozen," came the reply.

"And when did she first start going down hill?"

"About two weeks ago."

I pulled the chicken out of the box. She was like a hat rack, with her keel sticking out prominently from below. She was struggling to get her breath, her ribs heaving up and down with the effort. Behind her chest, her tummy was swollen and tight like a drum. Whatever it was, it wasn't good, that was obvious.

"Has she been laying eggs?"

"Oh aye, she's a great egg layer, she's laid an egg a day for the last few years without fail. But she's stopped now."

The reason for her problems was becoming more apparent. As with so many cases in veterinary, often the answer is in the history people give us.

I felt her all over, carefully palpating her abdomen. It was filled with fluid, but there was no hard lump to feel that might have indicated cancer.

"I suspect she has egg peritonitis," I said.

To make sure, I popped a needle into her tummy and was able to draw off some of the fluid. This helped the breathing almost immediately. Egg peritonitis is a common condition in chickens as they get older. Laying an egg a day cannot be easy, and in time the system can get worn out. This results in an egg going awry and, instead of passing down the tube correctly, it ends up in the tummy. There it sets off an immune reaction, causing large amounts of fluids to be produced. This reaction is sterile and so the chicken doesn't feel ill initially, but the pressure from the build up of fluid will slowly create difficulties in breathing and stop the chicken from eating. Sooner or later it will be fatal.

"It's not good, I'm afraid, there's nothing we can do." I explained about egg peritonitis.

"Is there really nothing you can do at all?" he replied.

"Well not really, though I suppose ..."

"Yes?" He looked eager.

"I suppose we could spay her."

I explained we could knock her out and open her up to remove her ovary and the entire uterus. If we could do that, and remove all the excess fluid caused by the aberrant egg, then we might be able to save her.

"I would like you to do that," he said adamantly.

Izzie filmed quietly as we operated. The operation itself wasn't going to be easy. The chicken was so poorly, that to be honest I never really thought it would survive the operation. She needed the smallest amount of anaesthetic gas to get her to sleep. Then we connected her up to a drip; with all that static fluid her circulation would be poor.

We plucked some feathers off her taught swollen side and surgically prepared the skin for where I was going to make my incision. As I cut through the muscle layer under the skin, the straw-coloured liquid came welling up, and poured out of the wound.

As the fluid drained away, the bird immediately began to breathe better. There were some obvious bits of eggs that I could remove, and then I took out the swollen ovary and the oviduct. This chicken would lay no more eggs.

It was an easy job from there to close the wound with simple stitches. The chicken was breathing strongly now, and I began to think she might just make it through the whole procedure.

Izzie, pointing the camera at me, asked me how I felt. This was something she often did, just to get me to wrap up the operation for the camera. She normally left me alone when I was actually operating.

I explained I had very mixed feelings. You see, it was the Monday after the big Africa poverty concert by Bob Geldof, called Live Eight. There he had been trying to raise awareness for the mass starvation and poverty occurring in Africa. Whilst here I was spaying a chicken. A common-or-garden reddy-brown chicken. It was a daft world. But when I got home, and was talking to Clare, she reminded me how much she and the others had really loved Army the mouse, the canaries, even Sharky the red-tipped shark.

"It may have only been *a* chicken to you, but to him, it was *his* chicken," she told me.

The little chicken did make a good recovery and went home safely. The owner himself had refused to be filmed, but was happy for us to film the operation. I was pleased we had been able to film it, as it demonstrated two things. First, the overwhelming love that people have for their pets, and second, how advanced veterinary science is becoming.

Chapter Twenty

Izzie saw straight away that the show had to have a beginning, middle and end, insomuch as the viewer found out what happened to every animal featured in that edition. Whether it is a happy or sad ending, the viewer is always left with a sense of 'closure', as they say in TV. Basically, they just want to see if old Mrs So-and-so's parrot made it or not. Not only this, she wanted to focus more on the owners and their emotions and involvement with their poorly pets. She also decided that it would be fun to expand the filming and shoot other work that I did, which was not just pure veterinary.

So when our local vicar asked me if I would be kind enough to open our local village show, and perhaps judge the pet show, I said I would be delighted, and asked him if he minded if Izzie filmed it. He was very gracious and didn't mind at all, but would check with the committee. They didn't mind either.

It was to be held in his back garden, later in the summer. It would be the normal affair, with charities organising tombolas, a flower stall and, of course, marvellous cakes made by the WI.

Sartorial elegance has never really been my thing, so Clare decided that this was finally her opportunity to go out and buy me a proper suit for the occasion. I have managed successfully to get through most of my life without a suit, borrowing one from my brother for his wedding and finally purchasing one for my own. I tried to convince Clare I already had a nice suit, but she said turning up in a morning suit might be a bit over the top.

Once Clare is on a mission, there is really no stopping her, and so within the week I was the proud owner of a new suit. As I always feel that spending money on clothes is a waste of money, she managed to avoid telling me the cost by claiming it was an early birthday present. Women are so cunning, aren't they! I was even more honoured when she also produced a Panama hat. This was something that she really felt was the correct thing for the local vet to wear when opening the local village show. I myself was not entirely sure and felt like I looked like Barbar the elephant. However, when Izzie and Clare get together there is no stopping them, and so I was persuaded to wear a hat to the grand opening. At least no one will recognise me, I thought.

The opening itself went off without any incident. Izzie was filming and had come with me in my car to get some footage of me arriving, so that the story would fit neatly into one of the episodes. The gods were shining on us, and it was one of those really lovely sunny Yorkshire days when you can stand on the wolds and see the White Horse far away on the other side of Ryedale. With the fête due to start at three p.m., I arrived early, perhaps too early, at two p.m. But then this was an important event in the local calendar and I hadn't wanted to be late. I took Izzie for a drive around the local countryside for a while to kill time. She patiently sat there filming shots of green meadows and hedgerows.

We arrived back at the vicarage at 2:45 and were met by the vicar. He thanked me profusely and then shoved a large megaphone in my arms and told me I'd need it. I wondered just exactly what I was meant to say. Everyone looked rather bored waiting for me, and I wished I had arrived earlier.

"I would like to start by welcoming everyone to the annual fête," I said pompously, and then dried up. I really couldn't think of anything else to say. At this point Tiger, now four years old, came to my rescue, by asking me whether that was it. I decided I should say something else, so helpfully said:

"I now declare this fete open."

The vicar, obviously rather more used to speaking to his parishioners than I, removed the megaphone from my sweaty palms, and took over. I swear I could hear him thinking 'stupid boy'.

He proceeded to tell them what was happening, where it was happening, and when the pet competition was. Finally he asked them all to spend a lot of money, as it was in a very good cause.

Oh God, I had forgotten about the pet competition I was going to judge. Or rather, I had hoped he had. I had never done anything quite like this before, and could only hope it wouldn't be too complicated. After all, this wasn't Crufts! However, my mind did drift back to that wonderful veterinary textbook, compulsory reading for all newly qualified vets, by James Herriot, in which he had to judge the local pet show. As I remember, in that story it hadn't gone very smoothly. I would have to be sure that my judging was beyond criticism.

I joined the boys as we wandered round the stalls, slowly spending vast amounts of money on things we either didn't need or had previously owned and donated to the stalls. The tricky bit was when they spotted one of their favourite toys and hadn't realised that Mum and Dad had parted with it.

Finally the time came for the pet competition and it was announced over the Tannoy. I was asked to go to the relevant area. There, in a motley line, were the competitors. Izzie patiently stalked me with the camera. My task was simple: all I had to do was decide which was the 'best pet in the show'. There was also to be a second and third prize, but no complicated sections, of best working dog and so on.

The first pet up was a small Jack Russell terrier brought by a young boy who had either mud or chocolate smeared carefully across his face.

"Good morning," I said, "and who is this?"

"He ain't got a name," came the reply. "He's a ratter."

"Ah good," I said as I leant forward to check the dog over.

"I wouldn't come near him if I was you," said the lad, "he can be a bit sharp."

At which point, as if on command, the dog leapt forward, quite obviously having decided that I needed my throat ripping out. He missed, but did manage to remove a small piece of my brand new suit.

"Lovely," I said, moving swiftly on to the next contestant.

Next up was a rabbit. The rabbit had a look of such fear in its eyes and had already peed down its mistress's dress, that I thought perhaps it would be better if there was a bit more space between it and the terrier, so I moved her to the back of the group.

This obviously didn't go down well with the mother, who immediately went off to complain to the management about my treatment of her daughter, who she felt was being discriminated against. This was not going well, I thought.

"Hurry up, would you please," said the next boy in the row. "My ferret's getting all arsy." I peered at the ferret, deciding that actually touching it would be tempting fate.

The next animal was presented in a small margarine tub. This would be safer.

"Who have we got here?" I asked the small girl in the pretty dress.

She smiled and said, "It's Albert, my pet giant land snail."

I thought I would try asking the owners questions to test their knowledge of their pets, and quizzed the girl whether she knew where giant land snails came from, expecting the usual reply of the pet shop.

"They are indigenous to Africa," she said, smugly. When I asked what sex Albert was, she gave me a withering look and told me they were hermaphroditic, as everyone knows. I think she thought I was an idiot. Ah well, that was one less fan now, I thought.

As I moved down the line asking questions, and avoiding touching anything in case I got more blood on my new jacket, I could find no one who knew as much about their pets as that little girl did about Albert. I asked little Johnny if he knew anything about his pet hamster, to be told they bite. I asked young Matthew about his snake, to be told they eat dead mice but would prefer live ones because it would be more fun. When it came to the end, I was very relieved. The rabbit, however, had gone.

How do you judge between snakes, mice, ferrets, a Jack Russell and a snail? I decided to go on knowledge of the pet, so proudly announced the winner to be the snail. My announcement was met with a rather stony silence. A snail, a lousy snail, I could imagine them all thinking. I felt I should give some explanation regarding my reasoning, but it didn't help. The audience had by now decided that it had been a fix. After all, the owner of the snail was, of course, the granddaughter of the local squire. And even she still thought I was an idiot. Ah well, I thought, really very little has changed since the days of Herriot.

Chapter Twenty-one

Sadly his foibles would prevent Kipper from making old bones, and as age crept up on him his neck became painful, more so when he was tired. In fact, towards the end his lopsided movement became so exaggerated that we would end up leaving him at home when we went on a walk. Medication had helped, but finally his liver began to fail. We had to put him to sleep. Clare and I both agreed that the time had come. It was a peaceful end, he was asleep on the sofa one Sunday morning when we let him go.

I am often asked if this is a particularly difficult part of my job but, you know, it isn't. Animals must have a good quality of life and maintain their dignity. Once these begin to go, it is important to help them. And when you can no longer help them, then it's time to let them go. They feel pain just like we do, and so the hobbling and limping that you often see in older animals is often because of the ache of arthritis. It never ceases to amaze me that some people don't think animals feel pain. Mammals are living individuals too! However, unlike us, they aren't able to sit and watch the telly, read a good book or do sudoko. They live for walks and cuddles. They know that going to the loo in the house is wrong, and when they are unable to control their bodily functions anymore then it really is time to call it a day.

Kipper hadn't reached this point but he was struggling more and more to get about. Staircases had become a complete no-no. We let him go, and dug a large hole in the ground next to Fly. Jack made a cross out of bits of wood and wrote in his young writing 'Here is Kipper, never forgotten'.

The next day was a Monday, and back to work. As I came down to make morning tea (a rash promise I had made to Clare in the heat of the moment, when she had had our first child, 'tea in bed for life'), there was no friendly wag of a tail to greet me. As every dog owner will confirm, there is nothing worse than no wagging tail to meet you in the morning. Tuesday was even worse.

Izzie asked me in the car what I was going to do, and I told her I was going to get another dog. Not another Kipper, that could never happen, but a new pooch with faults and foibles and all the traits that make up the more interesting of personalities in mammals. I decided the sooner the better.

It felt rather underhanded to look for another dog so soon after putting Kipper down, but I looked at it this way. He lived solely to give us pleasure, and vice versa. That's what owning a pet is all about. I reckoned the last thing he would want after his death would be for us to be unhappy, so I rang the good old RSPCA.

Elaine answered, and I told her that we had sadly had to let Kipper go. She was sorry but immediately told me that she had three little whippet crosses in. She knows me too well. I was hooked, and Izzie was delighted!

I decided to go off to the RSPCA that afternoon after the Zoo. But I was breaking a cardinal rule and had gone without even consulting the family. Izzie was filming as we arrived at the RSPCA, and she caught the instant rapport between me and the three scruffy little mongrels they had. I could only take one, so I chose the most bedraggled looking one. I picked her up and felt she looked just like a miniature Kipper, though darker in colour. Having paid the various fees, we put her into the back of the car and set off home.

I would need to tell Clare, and this was going to have to be handled correctly. Clare and I had been married a long time by now, and there was little that would fool her.

I rang and said that there was good news and bad news. She's not daft and immediately was suspicious.

"You're sounding very guilty," she said, "What have you gone and done?"

I confessed, trying to pass all the blame over to Izzie, arguing that she had led me on. But Clare is amazing and she took it well. Though I had a feeling that if this little puppy didn't meet with approval I would be driving back to the RSPCA later that night.

When I finally arrived home, with camera in tow, it was difficult to tell from her fixed grin and rigid greeting exactly how cross she was with me. But I knew it was bad. Guilty, as the new dog very quickly became called (as guilt was the theme of the day I'd had), was a star and immediately moved over to the kids with her long tail wagging. It hasn't really stopped since.

It was wrong of me to have gone without the family, I know, but it was very much impulse. But with hindsight it was probably a good idea. Had I taken Clare and the boys along to the RSPCA then, without any shadow of a doubt, we would have come home with three dogs, not just the one.

Now, when people stop and ask me where Kipper, my Hungarian twisted weasel hound is, I tell them he has sadly passed away. But I then point out my rather rare Hungarian straight weasel hound. This particular breed of dog is designed for more open countryside than the twisted variety!

In all the filming that I have done with Izzie, I don't think I have ever managed to shock her. She comes from tough stock. Mind you, on the day we had to remove the tail from Max the iguana she did look a tad perturbed. The iguana in question was a much loved and well pampered pet of the Shaws. They lived miles away but were referred to me from another veterinary practice after Max had injured himself. Max lived in a large enclosure. In fact, I think the owners had pretty well given over a whole room to him. There he could happily sunbathe in front of a tall window. However, as this doesn't provide the necessary ultraviolet rays that iguanas need, he also had a strip light to provide extra rays. Max preferred to spend his days in front of the window. One day, they decided to move his furniture around so that he could get closer to his strip light. Unfortunately, he got too close! He climbed up onto a branch, walked over and then fell fast asleep on the light. This had disastrous effects and he burnt himself badly. So badly that, although many of the affected areas of his skin healed well, the end of his tail began to go gangrenous. The tail was losing its circulation and the very end had already started to go black.

Unlike most iguana owners, who seem to begrudge everything that I ever try to do, the Shaws were great people who actually listened to me. They had struggled to bring their five-foot long iguana up in the car, but had managed, keeping him quiet on the back seat of the car. There was no way he was ever going in a box.

On examining the lizard, it was immediately apparent that there was only one thing that we could do: amputate his tail. His owners had already realised this and so were fairly well prepared for the news. Certainly with dogs and cats, when we have to tell owners that their pet is going to have to lose his or her tail, they are normally devastated. We all know and love a dog with a large wagging tail. Fortunately people who have reptiles are not so attached to their pets' tails (and neither would Max be soon).

I was concerned though. Max was going to end up with at least half of the length of his tail missing, and this may prove very shocking to both him and the Shaws.

Anaesthetising reptiles is a fairly easy job compared with many of the animals we deal with. They are hardy creatures, unlike birds for example, and very resilient. With the smaller ones, we often just hold their nose in anaesthetic gas and allow them to breathe themselves to sleep. With the larger ones, and the ones that can seemingly hold their breath for week or two, we normally inject them. They can also be quite obtuse, and if you accidentally overdose them then they can end up being asleep for days.

Max was easy, being used to being gently handled, so we managed to gas him to sleep quickly. Removing his tail was not going to be a normal run of the mill procedure. When we have to remove the tail from a dog or cat, we cut through the skin, then, after surgically removing and securing tendons and blood vessels, we cut through the bone. Finally the skin is carefully sutured over the stump to make a nice clean end. With lizards, it's completely different, they are designed to lose their tail naturally if a predator has hold of it. The tail can then regrow by a process known as epimorphic regeneration. The tail will naturally shear off through what is known as a break plane. The important thing for a planned amputation by a vet is to know exactly where the break plane is.

So the first step was to X-ray the tail. Having identified the break plane, I made a neat incision immediately over it, through the skin. I then literally ripped the tail off. This sounds gruesome I know, but the tail is designed to rip off in this way. The muscles tear apart in a very neat fashion and there is no bleeding. What I hadn't thought of doing was to warn anyone about what I was going to do. I pulled and I pulled, I ripped and I ripped and I twisted and I twisted. Rebecca looked slightly alarmed, but she trusted me; Izzie looked pale!

Suddenly the tail came free. Of course, I had also forgotten what happens when a tail is freed from a lizard. Once it is ripped off, it is designed to wriggle and wriggle to distract any predators so that the rest of the lizard can escape!

It's the only time I have ever managed to make Izzie look really pale. The minute I removed the tail, it started lashing from side to side. The irony of it was, of course, that the rest of the lizard was fast asleep. That made it all the more eerie. None of us expected the fast and sudden thrashing that occurred. Izzie felt so sick she had to prop herself up on the wall. I was fascinated, and wanted to be sure that she was managing to film it all. She's a true professional, and did of course manage to get it all on film. My next concern was that all the rest of the staff saw this rare phenomenon. I even managed to persuade my secretary to come in and have a look. I was acting like the horrible kid who's found a dead bird and is charging his friends five pence a look, and 10 pence to prod it with a stick. She thanked me sarcastically and, feeling queasy, left quickly, remarking that I was quite revolting. So what! I am that horrible boy, of course, so I thought it was great.

Having finally managed to dispose of the thrashing tail, I bandaged up the stump. We didn't stitch the skin closed, as reptiles heal very well on their own. Max could grow a new, shorter stumpy version of his old tail, but it would never regrow to the full glory of the old length.

Over the next few months Max healed well, and the Shaws found that Max the tailless iguana fitted into their car much easier now. Every cloud, and all that.

Izzie will still admit to this day that this was one of the more revolting things that she had ever filmed. Perhaps if I had warned them all it wouldn't have been so gruesome. Of course, it then wouldn't have been so much fun.

Although Izzie had managed to catch the iguana, sadly she was away when the bouncer came in with his snake. Reptile owners are a breed apart from others. They are often quite tough people and, in days gone by, many of them would, I am quite sure, have owned a pit bull terrier. I tell you, there're some reptile owners who make you feel like the nervous doctor from an old gangster film treating Mr Big's gunshot wounds: you hurt him, he'll hurt you.

The burly bouncer from Leeds was one of these people. In fact, he was in a league of his own and he really put the fear of God into me. I suppose it stems from the very first moment I saw him with his American carpet python wrapped round his shoulders.

The late, great Douglas Adams, in his *Hitchhiker's Guide to the Galaxy*, wrote about an SEP field that could hide an alien spaceship in plain view for all to see. The theory is that, if you saw a parked spaceship you'd probably ignore it, thinking it was being dealt with by somebody somewhere. SEP stands for Somebody Else's Problem.

The bouncer from Leeds had a snake with an SEP field. Let me explain.

The snake wasn't eating and had been rather subdued of late, according to the owner. I decided to admit the snake for tests that I would undertake the following morning. We didn't have a spare vivarium at the time, but fortunately the owner had one in the car. He lent it to me and departed, coldly telling me he 'knew' I would do my best. When morning came, the snake had vanished. It had successfully pushed the lid off, and wriggled out of the tank and vanished.

After several extensive searches it was nowhere to be found. Feeling incredibly unprofessional, I rang the owner and said I was terribly sorry but we'd lost his snake. He was alright at first, as he thought I meant that his snake had died during the night. When I went on to explain that his slithering chum had jumped ship, he was less understanding; in fact he became quite irate.

"Didn't you put a brick on top of the tank?" he shouted. "He can get out real easy you know."

That was obvious to me now, and I felt that perhaps the information about the brick might have been more helpful the evening before. I began to shake, and visions of visitations by Leeds' bouncers began to flash through my mind. It would not be pretty: we cowards bruise easily.

"I'm incredibly sorry; I'll buy you a replacement. How much was it?"

"Well, it was five foot of expensive carpet python. Three hundred quid minimum," he replied.

"How much?" I choked.

Anyway, after several more extensive searches, we decided the python was long gone and so I bought him a replacement. After all, it was my fault we had lost the snake. I sent him a cheque and thought the whole issue closed, making a mental note to myself to remember to buy some more vivariums and also some bricks.

Four weeks later I arrived at work one morning to find a note from the cleaner. It was the usual stuff, nearly out of this, need more of that, the mail's on the desk, etc. But there was little footnote which read 'Oh, and the snake's moved from above the drugs cupboard and is now living under the sink'. I nearly gagged on my coffee. The python had been living in my surgery for a month, rent free, and only the cleaner had noticed it. She thought it was just the new practice snake, or perhaps part of a new treatment regime of Matt's. A loose snake!

The python was quickly located and I rang the owner with the good news, secretly hoping he might offer me my £300 back. He answered gruffly:

"That means I've got two snakes now. You'd better get me another vivarium."

Chapter Twenty-two

Although we see quite a few snakes, we spend a lot of time looking after tortoises and so it was not going to be long before Izzie filmed one. But finding a good case wasn't proving easy.

These charming little creatures can make great pets, but they do not make for very exciting telly. Izzie stood through many tortoise consultations with me, but none of the cases were interesting enough to feature on TV. After all, how long can you hold an audience's interest by watching two people talking whilst standing looking at a small green box. You're not exactly going to get the excitement and danger of trying to grab an exuberant tortoise who doesn't want to be examined, are you? Not only that, none of them had made a dash for the door either.

Most commonly, we see tortoises when they have gone off their food. In general, this can be for one of two reasons, poor management or sex.

There are two very distinct groups of people who become tortoise owners. The first are those who seem to buy them almost on a whim and later realise they haven't the foggiest about how to look after them, or even what to feed them on.

These people either end up getting shot of them or keep them in a cellar on cat food.

Then there's the more thoughtful tortoise enthusiasts, who spend hours researching their subject and know all there is to know about our shell-backed chums and exactly how to make them happy.

In the wild, these unusual creatures live in a pretty harsh environment, surviving on a diet of high-fibre scrubby vegetation. They are not stupid by any means, and tortoises in captivity, being gluttons for high-protein 'tortoise junk food', such as cat food, learn quickly that if they hold out for something more tasty then their owners will often give in. In much the same way, my kids would rather live on a diet of fizzy pop and chips but I know that in the long term it won't do them the slightest bit of good. Junk food is disastrous for any creature, and tortoises are the same. They end up with all sorts of subtle problems, finally going off their food completely. What they really need is a high-fibre diet made up of food such as dandelions and fibrous types of lettuce.

Fortunately most tortoise owners are in category two: intelligent and caring people. They have read widely and thought long and hard before going out and getting their new friend. Interestingly, as a general rule, they differ markedly from other reptile owners in their personality. If they didn't have a tortoise, they would probably have had a cat.

Their tortoises are looked after immaculately, but even so it is difficult to mimic the natural conditions from which they come. They need warmth, the correct humidity and artificial sunlight if they are to be happy, and a good diet. But even then the lack of true seasons often means that the tortoise ends up confused about what time of year it really is. Female tortoises end up producing lots of potential eggs, or follicles, on their ovaries. These fail to mature properly into proper eggs and just sit there, each follicle growing to the size of a marble. Over time these 'marbles' accumulate and coalesce into large groups that look just like bunches of custard-yellow grapes. Gradually they occupy more and more space within the shell. There are very few signs from the outside of course, but finally the poor old tortoise stops eating, often because there just isn't any room left for food. The creature's other systems begin to shut down too.

This is a particularly common problem in the spring, when lengthening daylight hours and increasing temperatures tempt them to start trying to lay eggs. Some even go on to develop fully shelled eggs. This results in constipation-type symptoms, with the tortoises straining hard to pass the eggs with no luck. They may even strain so much that they end up prolapsing their cloaca, or bottom. Unfortunately, as there are so few visible signs to arouse suspicion, these cases often come into the surgery too late. The stuck eggs, and surplus bunches of follicles, all need to be removed.

Such was the case with Midge the egg-bound tortoise. I had been wanting to film one of these cases for two reasons. First, the problem is very common, and second the treatment is surgical and dramatic. This was a good one to film as not only was Midge full of follicles but she was also egg bound. The eggs are easy to see on an X-ray because they have a thin calcium shell. The follicles are more visible on a scan, where they appear like a mass of small water-filled balloons all sitting jumbled one on top of the other.

Having scanned and X-rayed Midge, we discussed treatment with her owner. She had been ill for a long period of time and was already weak and slow; and yes, I know that's ironic when talking about tortoises.

Surgery was the only option because the large eggs seen on the X-ray would never come out naturally. There were also so many follicles that they would need to come out as well. As there was no other choice, the owner agreed for us to proceed.

The procedure involved cutting a hole in the shell. The lungs of a tortoise occupy the top half of the shell, so the hole needs to be through the underneath.

Surgically it is not a challenging operation; however, the anaesthetic is far more demanding. Tortoises, like all reptiles, do not have separate body cavities like humans, but instead have one, large coelomic cavity. This means that, once you open up the cavity, the primitive lungs will collapse. To complicate the issue, the tortoise would be on her back, allowing all the rest of her organs to drop onto her lungs, squashing them. Incidentally, this is the reason why it is not a good idea to hold a tortoise upside down for long.

Not only would we need to be quick when we operated, we would need to breathe for Midge at the same time. She was anaesthetised by injecting a small volume of anaesthetic into the vein. Within seconds she was asleep. We popped a small tube into her trachea and connected her up to an IPPV machine. This machine delicately blows the animal's lungs up and down, filling them with a mixture of anaesthetic gas and oxygen. Now we could control her breathing. Once she was stabilised, she was turned onto her back. Time was now important; the longer she stayed on her back the poorer her chances of survival.

Once the bottom of her shell, or carapace, had been cleaned, we cut into it with a dental saw. It's glorified carpentry really. We cut a square out with a bevelled edge, so that when we put it back in place it would not fall through the hole but sit snugly back into position. The trick is to just cut through the shell, and the underlying bone, without damaging the underlying soft tissues of the body. As soon as we were through, we reflected the bony square up and out of the way. The custardy coloured follicles were easy to identify and remove from then on.

The fully developed eggs proved to be far more complicated. These eggs were hidden away within the folds of the reproductive tract. They were slippery, fragile and easily broken. Indeed, often before we operate, a tortoise can have cracked her eggs inadvertently by constant straining.

Even when I finally managed to get hold of one of the eggs in Midge it was so hard to get up to the hole it broke. I ended up having to remove the eggs bit by bit.

Once they were all out, I needed to suture closed the thin membrane that lines the cavity, and flip the flap of bone back into place. We then covered it in a waterproof coating of fibreglass. The shell of a tortoise is a living growing organ arising from the modified ribs of the animal. Underneath fibreglass the bone can regrow, filling in the hole over the next year or two. Nobody could ever accuse a tortoise of doing something in a hurry.

As soon as we had finished, Midge was put back the right way up. She had made it through the operation. Sadly, the whole experience proved too much for her and she was too weak to survive the recovery. Kindly, her owner agreed that, even though Midge had died, we could use the footage to demonstrate some of the problems we see in tortoises. I would add, though, that most tortoises that we have to spay do very well, provided we can catch them soon enough.

It was a busy day that day, as almost immediately after we had finished operating we were called up to the Zoo. Mandy the polar bear was not happy. She was now nearly 30 and had been living on her own for nearly two years.

The leap from treating one species to the other is sometimes quite surreal. It is, however, part of the fun of the job. One minute you're delving around in the insides of a tortoise and the next you're faced with a large polar bear. It's a challenging routine and keeps me on my toes.

When we got to the Zoo, Mandy's problem was obvious as she hobbled along on three legs, holding her left forelimb up in the air. Mandy was always happy to see her keeper, Ruth, as it almost always meant an extra treat.

She shuffled over to the bars to greet Ruth, thus allowing me to have a closer look. I had flashbacks of poor old Winnie, the old brown bear with arthritis, and mused that a polar bear would never fit in the back of my car.

Mandy had been fine since the day before, and had never shown any signs of arthritis up until now. Even through her thick coat the foot was visibly swollen, but try as we might to persuade her to lift her foot up for me to take a closer look, she wouldn't.

As you will remember, knocking out polar bears is not something that we do lightly and is certainly something that has left me with some pretty strong memories. So we decided to try lots of painkillers and antibiotics first before trying to look closer at the foot itself. Luckily, bears are easily fooled when it comes to giving them drugs; they certainly don't have the brains of primates and are nowhere near as suspicious as big cats. First, we gave her antibiotics hidden in a jam and fish sandwich. Although she enjoyed the sandwich, it didn't work; so we switched antibiotic and tried again, giving her painkillers as well. This helped, but the limping started again within a few days of finishing the treatment.

She began to lick the bottom of her foot, and there was now the odd spot of blood when she walked. This didn't fit in with arthritis and, as she hadn't responded to her medication very well, I began to worry about either a foreign body or even a tumour. We decided that we would need to knock her out and give her foot a closer check up. I knew I may want to X-ray the foot but, unlike with the old brown bear, taking her to the surgery was never really going to be an option. I would need to do everything there and be very organised about it as well.

Many things had advanced since the time the polar bear stood up on me and I ruined my best vet's trousers. We now had good lighting in the bear den, for a kick-off. Anaesthetics had moved on as well. I would no longer need to give her three darts; in fact, everything would fit neatly into just a single injection. This really made a significant difference. It was so much less stressful for both the animal and me.

Izzie coming with me added a completely extra dimension, though. We had never filmed the bears, and I still had in my mind the horrors of past bear anaesthetics. If Izzie was there and things went wrong, we could really end up in a pickle. My last moments might end up on some dodgy Internet site.

Thank goodness everything went according to plan.

Mandy was starved overnight, and it was easy to dart her with the modern rifle, the laser beam dot showing me exactly where I had to shoot. We waited the allotted 20 minutes, and then went through the usual rigmarole with the drain rods and finally the broom test. She was out for the count.

I also planned to clean her teeth, as well as check her over thoroughly, so had brought Diana with me. As soon as I had confirmed that she was fast asleep, we intubated her, passing a large horse anaesthetic tube down into her windpipe so that she could breath. Whilst Diana cleaned her teeth, I gave her the full MOT.

Much of the swelling had gone, but there remained an obviously infected hole in the bottom of the paw. I probed this, but could feel no foreign body. Disappointed that there was no simple solution to the problem, I X-rayed her feet. There might be an infection of the bone, which would mean long and protracted antibiotics. It would also be good to see how arthritic she was. I then cleaned and flushed the wound, pumping antibiotics throughout the infected area.

As soon as Diana and I had both finished, we woke her up.

Modern anaesthetics are wonderful. We can now wake animals up as soon as we like by giving them reversing agents. It's clever stuff, and means we no longer have to sit beside the cage for long hours if we have accidentally given them a bit too much.

She made a good recovery. The X-rays showed there was no sign of infection in the bone, and very little arthritis. I suspected that she had had a foreign body and that it had worked its own way out. Cleaning the wound up, and flushing it all through with sterile water and antibiotics, had worked. With all the dramas that I have had with bears over the years, the cameras had never been there, but finally Izzie's lenses had been there to catch the wonder of these magnificent beasts. Unfortunately the camera is never able to catch their indescribably horrible smell.

Chapter Twenty-three

You'll be getting the picture now that a lot of a zoo vet's work is birth control. It's particularly important with the baboons, because they go at it like no one's business. They're very noisy about it too. We had 60 baboons and no room for anymore, so I decided that, instead of spaying the females, removing the uterus and ovaries, it might be easier and more efficient to vasectomise the adult male baboons. A male baboon doesn't become sexually active until it's around four or five, so any over that age would have to have the snip.

The problem was that I had never tackled such a procedure before and was hard put to find any information about it. So I hit upon the bright idea of asking my own GP, Clive, how he did it on humans. Baboons, certainly in that department, aren't too dissimilar to us. I arrived at his surgery and his nurse asked me what it was regarding.

"It's too embarrassing to say," I replied.

She insisted, so I told her I was there about a baboon's vasectomy.

"No need to be sarky," she said, and sent me through with a stern look on her face.

I have known Clive for a long time, and so he wasn't at all phased. He explained the procedure, and I set to work. There turned out to be 27 male baboon vasectomies to do, and it took a couple of days. In fact, there was only one who was too young, a little ginger-coloured chap. He was left intact, with the new name of Lucky. Five years later, Lucky grew into adulthood and we had a sudden baby baboon boom and lots of little 'uns running around with the same hair colour as Lucky.

Nowadays, baboon birth control is a lot easier. We anaesthetise the females and put a small implant under their skin containing a human fertility management drug. It's a relatively quick and simple little operation. We knock the baboon out, make a small nick in her shoulder, insert the implant and seal the wound with skin glue. Fairly straightforward, really. Unless, of course, you accidentally jab yourself with the needle you've just used to anaesthetise the baboon. I managed to achieve this, accidentally giving myself a needle stick injury. Back I raced to Clive's surgery.

"What is it this time?" asked the nurse, a look of contempt on her face. "Want to know how to treat a chimpanzee's in-growing toenail?"

I smiled nicely and explained what had happened. She wrote on her notes, 'Matt Brash, prick'. Fair enough I thought; I did feel like one.

Clive was concerned because simians (apes) can carry all sorts of diseases, such as hepatitis, herpes and AIDS. Luckily I have a lot of vaccination in my system at all times; have to! But Clive still put me on a course of treatment to counteract all the diseases that were treatable, just to be sure. The only one he couldn't do anything about was AIDS. It was a waiting game. In six months time he could then perform an AIDS test to determine whether or not I'd got it. Clive tried to console me by saying if I did have it, we could at least get a fascinating paper out of the whole ordeal. It didn't help.

It was a long half year, but thankfully I was all clear. It does make insurance policy forms a problem though. They always ask if you've ever had an AIDS test and why, and I have to be honest and say yes, with an explanatory footnote.

'I jabbed myself with a needle whilst trying to stop a baboon getting pregnant' sounds more like a debauched party trick than the everyday life of a professional and competent vet. This job is a great leveller!

As the Zoo is one of the few places that has a collection of rifles that can be used to drop animals, we are often called upon to assist in capturing escaped animals. I always refuse to go and dart escaped or runaway dogs, as this would be too dangerous, both for the dogs and for the people close by. Whenever an escaped animal is darted, there is a period of time before the animal drops to the ground. This is often as long as 20 minutes. In the case of a dog, this length of time could be sufficient for it to run for a considerable distance, and tracking it is not always an option.

However, escaped horses and cows are usually another matter. But even with them the results can be unpredictable. I was once asked to knock out a horse that had escaped and had been running wild on the moors near Scarborough for nearly six months. Winter was coming, and there were concerns for its health with the approaching cold weather.

The rifle was loaded with Immobilon, powerful stuff, and we set off to stalk the horse and bring him in. Pretty soon I got a clear shot at him and fired. A clear hit. The horse should have slowed and fallen over, but he was so full of adrenalin he just carried on running. I shot him again. No result. Off he went.

The horse was crazy with fear and panic. He stayed just out of reach, and every time we got close he would run off. He ploughed his way through gorse bushes and hedges, and was beginning to make a mess of himself. If we kept after him, he could have ended up really injuring himself. Not only that, time was moving on and the drugs from the first dart would be wearing off. There was little chance that we would be able to catch this one, and at this rate we would end up having to shoot him.

I felt we could do no more, so we headed back to the car, leaving a disappointed farmer. As I walked back down the track from the moors towards my car, I heard a terrific noise behind me. It was the horse charging down the hill; the crazed animal ran straight past me and there was a loud crash. The poor animal had run head first into a tree. There it was stuck, with its head jammed in the V of the branches.

Not an ideal way to catch a horse, but it was then an easy matter to quickly put a halter over his head and lead him proudly back up the hill to the farmer. Sometimes the gods favour us!

The horse, hurt, distressed and very, very tired, walked calmly beside me now that he had been caught. He had a halter on for the first time in six months, and seemed to be reassured by it. A calmness seemed to settle on him now that he was reunited with the farmer, but it was probably complete exhaustion.

We were able to walk him back to the farm and, despite lots of bruises and small cuts, he made a good recovery. I suggested gently to the farmer that he kept a halter on the horse next spring when he turned him out.

Escaped cattle are usually much easier to catch. I say usually with feeling; the exception was, of course, the only one I have had to catch when I had Izzie trailing me with the camera.

One afternoon, as Izzie and I were sitting drinking coffee, the phone went. It was a desperate sounding farmer. He had tried everything to recapture one of his cows that had gone A.W.O.L. It was a bullock, bred for meat, and about 20 months old. These are wild at the best of times, but when they are separated from the rest of their herd they often get much worse and are almost impossible to handle. In this case, his bullock had escaped nearly six months earlier, moving down the valley and settling in with a bunch of sheep. His neighbour, who owned the sheep, was at the end of his tether, as the bullock was eating the sheep food.

He had tried everything in the book to recapture the bullock, but to no avail; even introducing three other cows to tempt it to join them, the bullock had preferred freedom. The farmer had tried herding the bullock into a barn, but he had broken free and galloped off up the hill. I was the last resort. Izzie and I set off in the car.

Without any doubt, the secret to darting animals is to be able to get close enough without them getting spooked. Once they have spotted you, you have often lost your best chance. In this case, the sheep farmer, a tall willowy man, had gained the confidence of the bullock as he had been feeding his own sheep every day. He would normally drive into the field in his red pickup van, so the beast was used to it. My best bet was to hide in this van. As there was no room in the cab for Izzie as well, she had to sit in the boot.

We drove through the gate, me keeping a low profile, whilst Izzie just grinned and tried to pretend she wasn't too uncomfortable. The farmer got out and concentrated on his sheep, deliberately ignoring the bullock. His sheep charged over, hungry for their treat of the day, and plodding behind came a tawny coloured bullock. Even from that distance I could see he looked as mad as a hatter!

I climbed out of the van, but could get no closer to him than about 30 yards. This would be a lucky shot if it was going to work. Unfortunately, on that day, the wind was blowing quite strongly. I fired, and missed, the dart sailing happily over his back to land in the grass on the other side.

Although I never hit him, he took one look at me and set off like a steam train for the horizon. We would have to have another go another day.

Three days later Izzie and I returned for take two. The same plan. We squeezed into the pickup and off we went. This time the wind was gentle and I was also able to get a bit closer. My dart was loaded with the dangerous drug Immobilon and, as I thought he looked as mad as a hatter, I had upped the dose a bit just to be sure we dropped him.

This time I managed to hit him, but not spot on. The dart had gone off course slightly, but I confidently told the farmer that the bullock should drop down asleep in 10 to 15 minutes.

Sure enough, five minutes later he was beginning to look slightly wobbly, so I think I turned proudly to Izzie and the camera and said "job done". Thank you to Izzie for editing that bit out, because it certainly wasn't anything of the sort. The bullock decided that all was not right. He put his head down and, with a serious rush of adrenalin, headed up towards the top of the hill. At the end of the field he never hesitated, and hopped drunkenly over the barbed-wire fence into a field of standing corn. He was off.

I raced up the field in hot pursuit, hoping that he was just giving one last spurt. But on arriving it became obvious that he had no intention of stopping, at least not soon. I could see that there was a tall hedge about 100 yards in front of him. Hopefully this would stop him. As I jogged after him, trying to keep my breath, I noticed Izzie lagging further and further behind. Obviously carrying a camera up hill was a bit of a swine; sorry Izzie.

Once we reached the top, he plodded along the edge of the hedge before ploughing straight through it. By this stage I had lost Izzie totally and realised that I was about to lose the bullock.

I got up to the hedge and in horror recognised where I was. This was the main Beverley to Malton road. A particularly straight bit, where the cars often travel at immense speeds. If one should hit the bullock then this could result in a great deal of carnage. Izzie was still nowhere to be seen, and worse still there was no sign of the bullock. In front was a field full of ripe rape, nearly six foot tall. He had disappeared into that. I was going to have get him out again on my own. What could I do?!

At this point Izzie and the farmer arrived in a car. We drove down a track to find the owners of the rape field. On telling them there was a slightly manic and partially sedated bullock loose in their field of rape, they didn't look very impressed. After a discussion between them and the sheep farmer, it was agreed that it would be too dangerous for us to try and find the missing bullock. There was only one thing left to do, and that was to shoot him.

At this the farmers' eyes seemed to open with delight. I don't think they often get a chance to go on a cow hunt. The next thing, a van appeared with four farmers hanging on armed to gills with guns. They sped off into the rape field, almost with a yeeha, and a few minutes later I heard a smattering of shots. Sadly the poor beast had been shot, but this really was the only thing to do in the circumstances.

Big animals that have escaped are running on adrenalin, and this can negate the effects of anaesthetic so potent it would kill a human in under a minute.

Izzie had filmed it all, and said phlegmatically you can't win them all.

Chapter Twenty-four

For some odd reason, people assume that just because I use a dart gun at the Zoo I must be an expert in all different types of armoury. Even so, it is not often that one finds oneself at the opposite end of a threatening gun: this time the gun was pointing my way.

Mr Hall was an 84-year-old dairy farmer who had lived all his life in our village. He had had 50 Jersey cows at one point, but was winding down the herd because of his old age. Despite his octogenarian status, he was still as feisty and Yorkshire as they come. He told me that he had once bought a Land Rover but couldn't 'be doing with it' because it had run out of petrol. He had only ever driven it the once into Malton, and there he had left it and caught a taxi back.

The first time I went to see him was because of a case of milk fever. A cow can get milk fever from lack of calcium because she is using up too much to produce her milk. The lack of calcium means that she collapses and is unable to stand. If untreated, the cow can die. But when caught quickly, with an injection of calcium into the vein, it is reversed easily and dramatically. The cow will literally stand up off the end of your needle.

On my arrival, I called out to tell him that I had arrived to examine his collapsed cow. I walked round the back of the house, only to have my way blocked.

"Are you any bloody good?"

Somewhat taken aback, I said, "Well, I qualified eight years ago. Not bad, you could say," and laughed.

I went to walk in again. Again he pushed me back.

"Can you hit a vein?" he demanded.

I assured him I could, and strode into the barn. I decided the chirpy vet routine wouldn't work here and I'd have to be a bit more assertive to earn Mr Hall's respect. I stood in his barn and turned towards him and my jaw dropped. He was holding a shotgun.

"You'd better be able to," he said, "I had to see the last bloody vet off with this."

Never have I felt under so much pressure to get a job done so efficiently. With shaking hands, I found the vein and allowed the bottle of life-saving calcium to flow in. Once I had finished, I stood up, and told him the cow would be back on her feet in a very short while.

He looked rather more relaxed now, and the gun was no longer held firmly in his hands but propped up by the wall.

"Grand lad, grand," he said, as he strode over to the cow. He knelt down and put his arms round her neck and gave her a big hug.

"I think the world of these girls you know."

Thank goodness within a few minutes the cow was standing again, with not a care in the world.

I didn't see Mr Hall again for a while, and when I did visit him, he was down to only two cows. This time when I arrived I was greeted with the more usual Yorkshire farmer's friendly smile.

He was worried as the girls were getting slower and slower. They were now in their late twenties. A very good age for milking cows. They had not had a calf for years, but were still producing a small amount of milk on a daily basis. Just enough for him.

I bent over one of them and ran my hands down her leg. Her joints were swollen with arthritis. We would have to give her something for the arthritis, I told him.

"I have been, vet'r'nary."

Out it all came. He had them on aspirin. Another farmer had told him it was quite good for cows with sore bones. The problem was the dose. They needed about half a packet of aspirins per day. As he didn't drive, not trusting the car, he would get a taxi into Malton every other day and go to the chemists. Since he was only allowed to buy one packet of aspirin at a time from a chemist, he would walk round town visiting all the shops, collecting one packet from each. He would then return to the farm. This would be repeated three times a week, and had now been going on for nearly a year.

"We can do better than that," I said as I pulled out from the car some bute, a horse arthritis drug. "This will make them feel much better and you will no longer need to go into town quite so often."

I have always believed that you should try every thing once, provided it's legal, of course. But perhaps aspirin for a year was a bit excessive.

Similarly, you shouldn't criticise things until you have at least looked at it and tried to understand it, and so it was with stalking. No, I don't mean hanging around in the bushes of Kylie Minogue's garden. I'm talking about deer stalking. Deer hunting.

This was not something I had ever really thought very hard about, nor was it something I was terribly interested in doing, until we were invited to go to Scotland stalking.

Stalking involves tracking red deer over the Highlands of Scotland. Once you're within range of shooting one, you do just that. It sounds a bit blood thirsty and barbaric, doesn't it? But I started thinking about my moral stance on the whole debate. I eat meat. I rather suspect that these red deer have had a far more enjoyable life than many of the chickens, pigs and cows that have ended up on my dinner table. Is it because a deer, or indeed a lion, elephant or racehorse, for example, has a romantic image? A kudos born of poetry, oil paintings and traditional songs that the likes of chickens don't have. How do you justify the difference between which animal is incredible and which is just edible? My head swam with the implications of it all, and I felt the only way to make up my mind was to accept the invitation. I defended my reasoning with, providing the deer didn't suffer, it was something I could, and should, experience.

The invitation was for a week's holiday right at the top of Scotland with a party of 10 others. I was particularly interested as managing deer was not a method of farming I had ever encountered, and I wanted to know whether it was anything like it is portrayed in the media.

On arrival, we drew straws as to which day we would go out stalking. Clare and I drew the short straw and got to go last, on the Friday. I felt this might be a mixed blessing. If the others had all been successful, then the chances of us being allowed to shoot a deer were going to be slim. But this could be a good 'get out' clause should we need it.

Effectively, stalking is farming with an extensive outside system. Instead of keeping all the animals inside in a barn, or penned in a field, they are allowed to roam freely over the Highlands. To manage the population, and provide venison, the deer must be shot dead, and there's simply no way to catch them. Herding them is completely out of the question. The trick in stalking is to get into the right position to be able to shoot the target cleanly. This is the job of the stalker, who will show you exactly how to do just that. This was the bit that I was most nervous about. The very last thing I wanted to do was to shoot and wound a deer. This is the only potential down side to extensive farming, as far as I can see. If you shoot and miss, not having achieved a clean kill, you run the risk of putting the animal through a lot of pain and suffering. Fortunately, the stalker also has a rifle, so that if a potential idiot like me shoots an antler or a tail off, he can quickly step in.

The week went by quickly, with Clare and I occupying ourselves with long walks around the loch and fishing. The other members of the party went stalking. All without success.

Finally Friday came, and we were really in a quandary by then. With no one to tell us about a kill, or how it left them feeling, we simply didn't know what to expect. Or feel!

We jumped into the back of a Land Rover and were taken down to the stalker's cottage for some practice with the rifle and a lecture on safety. The cottage was set in the middle of the Highlands in one of the prettiest locations I have ever seen. Set back and nestling in the side of a high mountain, it almost seemed to be part of nature itself.

As we climbed down from the car, a tall, wiry Scotsman, by the name of Archie, came out from the cottage and came to greet us. He took Clare's hand and pumped it solidly, then turned to me. His proffered hand stopped in midair as he stared at me.

"I know you," he said, in a thick Highland accent, "you're that vet off the telly, aren't you?" I replied affirmatively, although somewhat cagily. At that point I really began to wonder whether a vet should be doing this.

"Och aye, I love your series, I do, you're a dab hand with that dart gun of yours. There'll be no need to be showing you how to shoot then, laddy," he went on.

Aaaahhhhh! I thought, this was getting worse and worse. Now he's put pressure on me to shoot straight! Bloody marvellous. I was bound to miss and hit someone's pet Labrador or something now. I saw the headline in my head: 'Zoo vet shot my dog in deer hunting bloodlust gun fury fiasco!'

He whisked me off to look at his collection of guns and antlers. He told me he'd always admired the wapiti we have at the Zoo. He was after their antlers for his wall. I rashly promised I would send him a set when they die of old age. He beamed at the thought and stroked his gun. I'm sure he was thinking he could get the wapiti to part with the antlers much quicker than that.

Archie was a professional, and once he had chatted to us about how the day worked, we set of. They had a miniature tank, an Aga Cat, that would help carry any stags that we managed to bag down from the mountain. Don't bother bringing it, I thought.

Although the vehicle had plenty of seating, it was traditional that the stalkers should walk, so we followed the Aga Cat higher and higher up the mountains. Finally we reached the top, and lay there for a rest whilst Archie went off to find where his stags were. We were not to shoot just any stag we saw, he had picked out two he wanted taking out. I felt like a contract killer. The 'hits' were an older stag who was past his prime, and a younger one who was not a sufficiently good specimen to keep for the breeding season.

After we had been resting for about half an hour, Archie returned and said he had located the stags. They were about half a mile off, downwind in a perfect location. As I was to shoot first, he took me off, whilst the rest of the party remained hunkered down on the peaty crooks and crags of the moors.

Archie and I crawled and slithered the half a mile to the point where he had caught sight of the deer. They were still there, blissfully unaware of what was going on not too far away. He pointed out the old stag he wanted shot and passed me the gun.

"I've no need to tell you what to do, now have I," he chuckled quietly.

I just wished I had the same level of confidence that he had, and memories of my rather more disastrous attempts to dart animals sprang to mind.

Lining up the sights on the region of the stag's heart, I pulled the trigger. It was a horrid moment. I felt so sad for the big fellow, but I still pulled the trigger. My own heart was in my mouth, and I prayed I'd aimed well and finished him off instantly.

As I opened my eyes, all I could see was a stag disappearing over the horizon. Oh God! Had I wounded him or missed him altogether?!

To my utter disbelief, Archie patted my back and told me what a great shot that was, and that he really hadn't expected anything less from a zoo vet of such distinction. Apparently, I had managed to shoot the stag stone dead; it was the other one I had seen disappearing over the horizon. What a relief.

We collected the others, and walked over to where the magnificent, dead beast lay. He had hardly managed a step after he had been shot. It sounds horrible, really, doesn't it? But actually I think it is probably one of the kindest methods of farming I have ever come across. One minute he was free on the Highlands, his only worries food and sex; the next minute he was gone.

He had to be grallocked, have his intestines removed, immediately before they started to go off. The white omentum (part of the gut) was then hung on his antlers so that we would be able to find him easily on our way back. And so we left him to collect later.

Two more stags were shot that day. They asked me if I wanted to shoot another, but one would do for me. I had now experienced the process first-hand and felt no need to do it again.

We dragged the stags back to the vehicle and came down from the mountain. The stags were taken to a special room, where they were dressed ready for the butchers. There was to be no waste, however, and even part of the pelvis was carefully removed and frozen. As was the penis! This particular part of the anatomy is a favourite amongst the Chinese down in London! After I learned this, I always double-check that 'crispy duck' on Chinese menus is what it says it is, and not a spelling mistake.

When we got back to Yorkshire, I managed to keep my side of the bargain as the Zoo had a pair of wapiti antlers in stock and I posted them up to Archie. I have always wondered whether Archie has the antlers of the deer I 'hit' proudly mounted on his wall next to all the others, and tells people that this one was shot by the Zoo Vet himself. I have never returned; I don't have the blood lust to want to do it twice.

Chapter Twenty-five

As I take you on a tour of my life and times in the world of veterinary ups and downs, there's a number of recurring, supporting characters I simply must introduce to you. Folk that, thankfully, are a big part of my life and enrich, inspire and enhance not only myself but every person and beast they touch.

This book would never be complete if I didn't allocate one whole chapter to one person. This lady is really one of the most remarkable people I have ever met in my whole career. Her name is Jean Thorpe and she works voluntarily, and tirelessly, in the treatment of injured wildlife. She takes in all manner of wild creatures that have been found rejected, shot at, hit by cars or fallen foul of bigger beasts. Foxes to deer, badgers to owls, you name any British wild animal and Jean will have treated one. She does her darnedest to nurse them back to health and return them to the wild. She's a quite amazing woman but, despite all our efforts on an almost yearly basis, the government won't give her medal. Maybe I shall have to donate some money to the Labour party! But rather than waste it, maybe I should just throw Jean a party.

I first met her when I received a call from the RSPCA a long time ago when I was still working as a junior assistant in Beverley. It was the middle of the week, when Inspector Stuart Dodds rang.

"We have seized three dogs that we suspect have been involved in badger baiting," he told me. "Can I bring them down for you to examine?"

I knew little about badger baiting at that time; in fact I don't think I had ever really heard of it. It is a particularly nasty and cruel practice, to call it a sport is incorrect, that only man could invent. It was banned a long time ago but is still practised by idiots who seem to have nothing better to do with their lives. In essence, a terrier is sent down a badger sett to locate a badger. The terrier normally wears a locator collar with a small transmitter the size of match box. When a terrier finds a badger, it will stop and bark at it. The men above use a receiver to determine exactly where their dog is and then dig down to find it. Having broken into the tunnel, or pipe as it is called, they pull out the dog.

They then use grasping tongs, or some such implement, to grab the badger and wrench it out of the ground. To stop the terrified creature running away, it often has its back legs broken. Terriers, often Patterdales and lurchers, are then set upon the badger to fight it.

Badgers have a very particular way of fighting. They curl up in a ball, to protect their groin, snapping and biting upwards at their aggressor. So any injuries the assailant will sustain are always similar: puncture wounds and rips to the flesh on the front legs, neck and lower jaw. Often the dogs suffer hideous injuries, with their lower lips ripped off and teeth broken. The brock is a powerful animal when cornered, and a tough fighter, and it's the fighting spirit that the baiters want to watch. Just why badgers are such powerful fighters has always been a mystery to me. True, they belong to the Mustelidae family, and so are related to the carnivorous stoats and weasels, but the main diet of badgers is worms. How much of a fight do they have to have with a poor lowly earthworm? But I digress.

The badger of course ends up dying. What enjoyment anyone could ever get from this practice is completely beyond reason. Badger baiters are sad, inadequate little men and life is wasted on them.

Back in the early 1990s, Ryedale and the surrounding countryside was sadly one of the centres for the practice of badger baiting in England. There were two main reasons for this, the high density of badgers in the area, and the sandy soil, which made it easy to dig down to find the badgers.

When Inspector Dodds rang, and explained that he had three dogs in his custody, I said that of course I would look at them. This was the start of a very long road as I joined forces with many others in trying to get rid of this hideous blight upon human decency.

The officer arrived with the three dogs in the back of his white van, followed by a battered old blue estate car, the boot of which was tied shut with string.

Out of the second car climbed a tall, stocky, handsome lady. She was wearing welly boots and a crumpled barbour, and had a weather-beaten solid face. This was Jean Thorpe.

She took my proffered hand and shook it vigorously. She looked deeply into me. I knew I was being weighed up: how good was I going to be?

"Come on in," I said, "and tell me what's happened."

We went into the consulting room, and after I had furnished us all with coffees, Stuart turned to Jean and said, "You tell". Jean told us.

"At about 11:30 last night I had a phone call from a farmer to say that he had seen a white van parked suspiciously on the side of the road, near a wood. As he knew that there was a badger sett up there, he rang me. I went up there with a torch and had a look in their van. The boot was empty except for some dog crates and a couple of spades. I walked up to the sett and found the buggers digging. There were two of them, one digging, and one shining a torch down the hole. I could see some dogs tied to a tree, but not much else. It's not a big sett, just an outlier probably, and I don't think they had been there long. I called the police, and waited."

I stared at her. This woman had to be stark, staring bonkers. Who in their right mind would ever go alone into a wood in the middle of the night, looking for criminals armed with spades and who knew what else? Over the years I was to learn that this was nothing to Jean. If she was going to stop them, then that was what she had to do.

"The police are a dozy lot, so I walked back down to the car to wait for them. If they had turned up making too much noise then the diggers would have had enough warning to get away, and I wanted this lot."

"When the police arrived we went back up the track to the sett and got them. They had three terriers with them, a couple of spades, and some hessian bags. There was no sign of any badger, though. I think they had only just started digging, but one of the terriers has been injured. This makes me think they might have been at it elsewhere this evening. What we need to know is whether these dogs have been baiting or not."

As is common practice, when the police arrest people with animals, they call the RSPCA to take control of the creatures. The RSPCA had picked up the dogs later that night and now wanted a full veterinary health check to see if they were alright. I was to treat any injuries, and if I could lend any weight to proving they'd been used to fight badgers, then so much the better.

"Well, let's bring the first dog in," I said.

The first was a leggy Patterdale terrier, as many of these badger-baiting dogs are. He was in a sorry state. I stooped over the table and began to check him over. His lower lip was badly ripped and hung from his jaw bone, the white bone exposed to the air. It had stopped bleeding, but there were clots of blood hanging like string from the flap of skin. In his mouth, dark red holes showed where teeth had been lost. But despite these apparently horrible injuries he looked quite happy and perky, and the rest of him was fine. He stood on the table, wagging his tail. It is one of the more extraordinary things that I've discovered about these dogs: they might have a vicious streak in them when it comes to meeting badgers but when meeting people they are as nice as pie.

"We will need to treat this," I said to Stuart.

"What about the cause, can you see any badger hairs or anything?" Jean chipped in hopefully.

If I was to prove to the magistrates that these injuries had been caused by a badger, then I needed to show that the dogs had definitely been in contact with a badger. I turned to examined him again. He was smattered in reddish brown mud, and had obviously been digging, but that was not really a crime. There were no visible signs on the outside of badger interference, apart from his wounds. This was the first time I had ever come across these types of injuries, and couldn't say for sure what had caused them. Stuart looked crestfallen; Jean looked grim.

It then occurred to me that if he had been fighting with badgers, he may well have had a mouthful of badger at some point. However, checking the interior of his mouth yielded no clues: not a single badger hair.

"I am going to make them sick," I said, much to Stuart and Jean's surprise.

"There is a drug we use to sedate dogs called Rompun. It's actually a cattle sedative, and it has a nasty side-effect in dogs of making them vomit. We use it when we suspect a dog might have been poisoned, which is quite horrible, but better out than in!"

My reasoning was that, if we made the dogs vomit, we could see if they had ingested any badger hairs. Then we should be able to prove they had been in contact with a badger.

"I can sort out his wounds whilst he's sleepy," I added.

Jean's eyes narrowed as she finished her weighing up and began to draw conclusions about me. I felt I was beginning to pass her test.

I went and found some Rompun and proceeded to inject the dog gently in the back leg, whilst Stuart held him. The dog never twitched and I hoped I was passing his test too, so we could save him from any further injustice.

Sure enough, a couple of minutes later, the dog threw up on the table and then began to wobble, before sliding gently down. I put him in a kennel, and turned to look in the vomit. There, amongst some bits of partially digested chicken, were clumps of hairs. I tentatively poked my way through the mess, and picked one out.

Chapter Twenty-five

"Badger?" I said, tentatively.

"Badger," said Jean with a large grin all over her face. "Gotcha."

I put the hairs carefully into a sample pot and then, for completeness sake, put the rest of the vomit into another sample pot. Having cleaned the table, I brought the poor sleeping dog back into the operating theatre and set to sorting out his injuries. We cleaned the mud from around his face and lip, and I sewed the dangling flesh back into place to restore his good looks. We gave him covering antibiotics and a painkilling injection, and put him back into the kennels to wake up.

All three dogs were treated in the same way, and badger hairs were retrieved from all of their stomachs. Although Jean was sure the hairs were definitely from a badger, I wanted to make our case watertight in order for it to stand up in court. It would be me giving the evidence on the identification of the hairs, and I really wasn't sure that I was much of an expert on different hair types. So I posted the hairs off to an actual expert in Bristol, a leading authority in this field. He would carry out electron microscopy on the hairs to identify them. Months later, his report confirmed our initial diagnosis. Meanwhile, the RSPCA went ahead and charged the men for interfering with a badger sett, causing unnecessary pain and suffering to their dogs, and allowing their dogs to fight with a badger.

The case finally went to court. I hadn't seen Jean in the meantime, so went over to say hello. She met me with her normal, large smile and asked me if I was ready for our court battle. I lied and said I was. In reality, I was terrified. I'd never been to court before. Heck, I'm one of those people who feels guilty if a policeman looks at him. I get nervous watching *The Bill!* What was I going to be like in a court of law!?

The cases seemed to drag on for hours before we were called. We sat outside the courtroom on hard Victorian wooden benches. Perceptive as ever, Jean sensed my nervousness and kept me talking to take my mind off matters. She told me all about badgers, badger baiting and a million other things. She got me hooked. Finally she was called to give evidence on how she had found the men and called the police. Then the police went in and gave their evidence, then Stuart and, finally, it was my turn.

As I went in, Stuart leant over and whispered, "It's all down to you mate."

No pressure then. Cheers, Stu, yeah!

The case seemed to hang on whether we could prove that the dogs had been fighting with a badger. The defence had argued that the men had been out lamping. Their dogs had chased a fox, but it had gone to ground in the badger sett. Although they knew it was a badger sett, they had thought that it was an old disused one, and not recently inhabited. A good defence, unless you can prove that there was a badger there at the time. We had not found a dead badger anywhere in the vicinity, and the area had been so dug about and trampled any recent signs of badger activity had been long since disturbed.

I stood up in the crowded court room and looked around. The room was oak panelled and had a musty smell. You could have cut the tension with a brick! The benches at the back were crowded with reporters scribbling madly on tiny notebooks. Three stern-looking magistrates sat behind a long, imposing bench at the other end. In between was a collection of lawyers, sitting at desks piled high with books and papers scattered in an apparent state of chaos. All-in-all a singularly intimidating scene; but I suppose that's the point. I concentrated on staring at the oak lip of the witness box, which I gripped with white-knuckled hands.

I held the *Bible* in my right hand and took the oath. Promising to say only the truth, the whole truth and nothing but the truth. I ran through my evidence. I explained how Stuart and Jean had brought the dogs to me and I had examined them. I described the horrendous injuries I had found. They asked me to elaborate on what I thought might be the cause, but I did not feel qualified to give an opinion. Finally I went on and explained how I had made the dogs vomit and how we had found the hairs.

As I gave my evidence, I relaxed and dared myself to look around. Two things were noticeable. The look of disgust on the magistrates' faces as I had described the terriers' injuries, and their look of horror as I had told them of the badger hairs in their stomachs.

I knew that we had just proved, with reasonable certainty, that these lads had been badger baiting. The look of quiet satisfaction on Jean's face was a sumptuous reward.

The men were convicted and sent to jail. Their dogs had been confiscated, and were to be found new homes. For Jean and me it was the start of a long relationship with each other and wildlife. Since then I have been involved in more than 30 cases of badger baiting, often with Jean, and she more than anyone else has managed to rid our area of this gruesome hobby.

Fortunately we do not have to meet in the law courts so often these days and, although I regularly see her with other wild animals, I only really see her regarding badgers when we have gone to watch them. We go and watch badgers at a hide in Dalby Forest, the same place I took the BBC, Trude and Charlie years before. I still go regularly with the kids and remember being delighted one evening because Jean was there as well. This meant that the kids would have an extra special lesson that evening.

I spent the trip up to the forest telling the kids how quiet they must be when we were there. If we were too noisy, then we would scare the badgers away.

The hide is a converted caravan, into one side of which a large window has been cut. It sits hidden in thick woodland, with the sett lying 30 yards away, down a steep bank. After the cubs are born in the early spring, the area is baited with food, to encourage the badgers to come and feed up near the caravan.

One must arrive early, settle in on a hard wooden seat, and then wait patiently. Badgers do not come out to order, but normally appear around dusk. Waiting is not always an easy thing with children. However, they were being great, as quiet as mice. The only thing that disturbed the peace was an occasional 'cheep, cheep'. It was difficult to pin down where it was coming from, but it was definitely there. It would last for a minute or so, and then there would be silence again for a while. Jean was also not her normal self, and rather fidgety.

Finally Clare managed to track the noise down. Jean was feeding a nest-full of baby birds. As they needed feeding every 15 minutes, she had tucked them into the top of her bra, where they would be warm and she could easily reach to feed them. As the chief of police was also with us, she didn't want to draw attention to herself, and was trying to feed them surreptitiously. It didn't work. Once the boys found out, they were far more interested in what Jean had stuffed down her jumper than in anything else. Jean, however, took it all in her stride. But that's Jean.

Chapter Twenty-six

So I discover I need two chapters to write about Jean. I was (and still am) in awe of her, and sometimes feel like a bumbling puppy trying to please its master when I'm dealing with her. If truth be known, I could write a whole book on Jean, but I shall have to leave that to her.

After the case of the badger baiting dogs, I didn't see Jean again for a while, but not long after I had moved up to Malton she arrived one day with a kestrel under her arm, wrapped in a towel.

"Do you think you might be able to do anything for it?" she asked.

In those days, before we had the anaesthetic gases we have now, we used to have to anaesthetise them by injection. A combination of two drugs given in the muscle would send them to sleep. Too much, however, and they would easily go to sleep forever, so it was always a tricky and worrying procedure.

"Let's have a look," I said, gently taking the bird from her.

It had broken its right wing, and would need fixing if it was ever to fly again.

"I can give it a go," I said, after looking at the bird. "But the anaesthetic will be risky."

"You can only do your best," she replied, leaving the bird with me.

After she had left, I put the bird in a small cardboard box and set about getting organised. I would need to X-ray it first, then I would be able to work out how to fix the fracture. I had never done this before, but knew that if I was to have half a chance then I would need to have everything ready before we even started.

The graceful, sleek, bird of prey sat quietly and patiently looking up at me from the bottom of the cardboard box. I picked it up and injected a tiny volume of anaesthetic into its leg muscle. I closed the lid on the box and gave the bird 15 minutes of peace and quiet to go to sleep.

On my return, the bird was lying gently on its chest. Initially I thought it had died, but there was a small movement as it breathed. I placed its head in a face mask so that it could breathe oxygen. As quickly as I could, I X-rayed its broken wing. I wasn't sure how long I would have before the bird awoke. The X-ray showed that there was a fracture through the humerus, the upper wing bone. The edges of the break were jagged, so I knew that if I could manage to get a metal pin down through the middle of the bone, to keep it all in line, then it should repair.

I pulled the feathers out over the position of the fracture. It always seems harsh to do this rather than clip them, but it does at least mean that new feathers will grow quickly. If we cut the feathers, it can take several years for the stumps to moult out.

Still working as quickly as I could, I cleaned and disinfected the area. A small incision through the skin revealed the jagged ends of the broken bone. They stared up at me, gleaming white with a reddish pink, hollow marrow. It was easy then to slide the pin down through the centre of the bone and out through the elbow joint. Once I had lined the end of my pin up with the fracture line, I manipulated the two ends of the bone together into a straight line and slid the pin back down the marrow.

The bone now lay perfectly in a straight line, with the pin sticking out through the skin by the elbow joint. I cut this short, leaving an inch of it standing proud. Once the break had repaired I would be able to remove the pin by grasping this end. Still worrying about how much longer I had before the bird woke up, I quickly stitched the skin wound closed with two small stitches.

I gave the bird some painkillers and antibiotics by injection and sat back feeling jolly pleased with myself. I had just fixed my first broken wing on a bird. I couldn't wait to tell Jean. Now all I needed was the damn thing to wake up.

Several hours later, and several more coffees, I was still staring at the bird. It lay peacefully on the table, breathing softly, but making no attempts to wake up. Not even when I tried the brilliant line, 'Why don't you come round for coffee?' to it.

There had been no need to rush the operation after all. The others all went home, and in the gloom of the evening I sat there puzzling over anaesthetic doses for birds and wondering how I could do it better.

It was predictable, really, that having sat there all that time, the bird would finally wake up the moment I went to go and have a pee. On my return, I was surprised to see my patient no longer on the operating table but now sitting huddled on the floor looking miserable.

"It's awake," I said beaming down the phone, "it's awake."

"I'll come and collect it," replied Jean.

"No don't worry, I'll drop it off, it's on my way home."

I carried the box carefully to my car and went to Jean's house, for the first of many, many visits. She lives down a cul-de-sac in Norton, which reminds me of Privet Drive, the close in which Harry Potter was brought up by the Dursleys. Apart from the overgrown hedge and tall willowy trees, you would never guess what an Aladdin's cave hides round the back. Her back garden is a menagerie of recuperating wildlife in various states of repair and rehabilitation. Down one side are tall aviaries, hidden by layers of overgrown ivy and shrubbery. Hiding within at that time were recovering owls and a jackdaw. Opposite are converted cages and boxes of all shapes and sizes, containing 'all creatures great and small'.

There are countless creatures roaming the Yorkshire countryside, alive and well, thanks to Jean. So good is she that I honestly would not like her to visit the dinosaur room in the Natural History Museum. Jean's love, care and expertise in the treatment of wild animals would have the buggers back on their feet in no time and the streets of Britain would be crammed with fresh-faced brontosauruses and the like.

On arrival, Jean ushered me to her adapted garage, carefully taking my charge from me. She placed it into a converted rabbit hutch for the night.

"I'll give it some fluids and food later tonight," she said. "But first it needs a bit of peace and quiet after all your poking about."

"You will have a coffee, won't you?" she asked. And without waiting for an answer, she strode off inside.

Inside the kitchen there wasn't an inch of spare space. Apart from the normal kitchen bits and pieces, the room was filled with small boxes that squeaked as you went near them. From behind blankets came rustling sounds, and I quite expected some arctic creature to appear from the fridge as she opened the door for the milk.

"Have you eaten?"

Before I even had a chance to reply, she had pushed a baby hedgehog out of the frying pan and back into its box, and was slapping some bacon on to cook. I was treated to the first of many, many bacon and mushroom sandwiches. No one else makes them quite like Jean. You can almost taste the hedgehog.

Six weeks later I dropped in to see how our bird was doing.

"Oh, grand," she said, "absolutely grand. Come and look see."

There was the bird, no longer looking hunched and miserable, but hopping about from perch to perch, in one of Jean's outside aviaries.

"It's nearly ready to go," said Jean.

"I would like to check it over first, and we must take the pin out," I said pompously.

She grinned. "I'll get the bird then," she said, humouring me.

Jean got her towel and, expertly catching the bird, brought it over to me. I inspected my handiwork. The pins are normally pretty loose by this stage, and will slide out easily without having to put the bird under anaesthetic.

As I handled the wing, the bone felt strong and hard. The feathers were growing back, but of the pin there was no sign.

"Where's the pin?" I gasped.

Jean continued to grin. "It disappeared a few days ago. It must have removed it itself, that's why I knew it was ready to go."

"Would you like to watch?" she added.

I nodded enthusiastically and later that evening, when there was still just an hour or so of light, we drove up to where Jean had first found it. There would be just enough light for the bird to find its way round and then get settled before dark.

"You let it go," she said, "you fixed it."

It is one of the greatest moments one can ever have, to have mended a wild animal and then to let it go back into the wild. It is such a lovely feeling. For the bird, though, the romance of the moment was lost and it was crashing about in its box trying to get out. Such a difference from when it had first come to me all those weeks ago. As I opened the lid it shot off like an arrow, without even so much as a 'About time an'all. And you've got cold hands, mate!' But watching it fly to freedom was reward enough.

I returned home thoughtfully. It had been a great success; to successfully treat and then release is not easy. Jean is particularly skilled in her job as she has a very practical approach to rehabilitating wildlife. Imprinting and socialisation are the main problems that all wildlife rehabilitators face, and she manages to minimise the danger successfully.

When humans have close contact with young wild animals, 'imprinting' can occur. This is when an animal perceives its 'carer' as its mother, and indeed thinks itself to be human. Avoiding overhandling and mothering them is a difficult balance to maintain, particularly if they're babies and look cute. Jean gauges her influence cleverly to ensure that all her adopted children go back into the wild with the minimum of heartbreak on both sides. And she does this admirably!

With domesticated pets it's not a problem. Who doesn't mind a big warm dog sleeping in their bed of a cold winter's night? Maybe a parrot copying the catchphrases of *Little Britain* could be a bit embarrassing during a dinner party, or a visit from the vicar, but on the whole it's OK. With wild animals that are to go back to the wild, it is important that they maintain their sense of what they are. Once imprinted, they will lose their ability to fend for themselves and their ability to mix with their own kind.

Socialisation is another problem. This is when an animal loses its fear of humans. Whilst this may not matter if it is a robin, it becomes more of a problem with a badger or a deer. Not everyone wants a deer sitting on their doorstep waiting for breakfast every day!

Over the years I have had many adventures with Jean, with all sorts of wildlife problems. So because of our times bashing badger baiters, retrieving fishing line from a swan's throat, or even tending a rabbit who had had a barney with a passing car, or a 'bad hare day' as they call it in the bunny community, when we started filming *Zoo Vet* it was only a matter of time before we ended up calling upon Jean.

When Jean brought in a tawny owl with a broken wing, I hoped it would make a fascinating story with a happy ending. Sadly, many of the wild animals we look after are unable to be returned to the wild and so have to be put to sleep. Luckily, Mr Owl lived to fight another day: so it was good telly!

Upon checking the owl, it had obviously not broken its wing as badly as the kestrel had, but it still needed treatment. I confidently knocked it out, whilst Izzie filmed, took a quick

X-ray, and had the bird strapped up and awake all within minutes. The bird spent a month recuperating at Jean's before she let it go, near the Buddhist monastery in Pocklington. This bit of filming was one of the endings in the last series, and certainly was one of the most memorable. Owls tend to be more relaxed in a box, so we were actually able to take it out by hand and then let it go. Izzie filmed it as it disappeared off into the gloom of the evening. I think I would like to be a wildlife rehabilitator when I grow up.

One of the other animals we filmed with Jean was a baby badger. This little chap had been found in a garage, stranded after a spate of floods. It was tiny, bald and pink. Its eyes hadn't opened yet, and without immediate warmth and food it would die quickly.

Jean took it in and fed it every two hours, day and night. The patience of a saint. Izzie and I occasionally dropped in to record its progress. After a couple of weeks, the badger had opened its eyes and was beginning to snuffle its way around the cage. Jean was feeling sad; her time with the little fellow was coming to an end. It was growing up and, to avoid imprinting, needed to be put with badger brothers and sisters. The following week, Jean was planning to take it down to Somerset to a badger rescue centre. There it would be brought up with other badgers. First it needed to be tested for tuberculosis. This nasty bacterial disease is the scourge of both badgers and cattle and, if it was positive for TB, there would be no future for this badger.

Jean sat it on her lap and, whilst it suckled on a baby bottle of warm milk, I slid a small needle into its vein and drew some blood. All the time its little eyes never left Jean. It had imprinted on her. Her strength of will in allowing it to go was immense. The little badger that she had now looked after for six weeks adored her and would have happily stayed with her for life. But her philosophy was rigid, and correct. If you cannot release wild animals back to the wild, then you should not try to save them at all. It is a sound philosophy, for what life can there be for a wild animal with an irreparable injury to spend the rest its days in a cage or walking round a garden. The animal would become a prisoner of compassion.

Chapter Twenty-seven

I am often asked what is the most dangerous incident that has happened to me. That's easy, the ruddy polar bear: sorry to go on and on about it, but it was truly terrifying. I also get asked what is the most painful injury that has happened to me, and that too is easy. Hamsters!

All vets have a pathological fear of hamsters. These tiny creatures carry an extraordinary powerful punch for their size. Quite remarkable really. They are the most tricky of animals to handle; they seem to have the ability to turn around within their own skin and get into the best possible position so that they can sink their not inconsiderable teeth straight into your fingers. It really, really hurts! So it wasn't surprising when one day one of my colleagues came through holding his hand high in the air, wrapped in white kitchen towel, with thick blood oozing and seeping through it. It looked like something from a horror film, but I instinctively knew it was a hamster bite. Had to be, by the look on his face. One of pain mixed with fury and embarrassment.

He told me it had been little Charlie's hamster, Misty, a case he'd been treating all week and had been brought in for one last check-over. Misty had had wet tail, the hamster equivalent of gastroenteritis, which is often fatal. We had been treating it daily with injections and slowly managed to pull the little fellow round.

The owners, little Charlie and his parents, were over the moon the hamster was finally eating on its own and nearly back to normal. My colleague checked Misty over carefully and then popped it back in the little shoe box that they had brought it in. He leant over the table to tell them that Misty was going to be alright, when the little bugger poked its head out and, seeing his unguarded finger, sank its monster-like teeth into it.

"What happened?" I asked sympathetically.

He shook his head solemnly and said, "I did what everyone does when you get a sharp pain in the finger, I pulled my hand back with a start. Unfortunately Charlie's hamster was still attached and sailed over my shoulder and hit the wall with a thud."

I winced and enquired as to the state of the hamster.

"Well, it's back in its box, and on painkillers and oxygen at the moment, but it doesn't look good. I had told the owners it was going to be alright, but I'm not so sure now. Amazingly they seemed very understanding. What shall we do?"

I went and took a look at Misty, who was curled up in a ball with its mouth wide open. It really didn't look good. I advised keeping Misty in for a few days, treating it for shock, and, if he was at all able, my colleague should keep what was left of his fingers crossed.

We were lucky; Misty did make a full recovery. While I always tell my vets and nurses to keep count of their fingers when a hamster is in the building, I cannot guarantee that another 'hamster flick' incident will never happen again. It's part of being a vet, I'm afraid. I have to admit that the hamster flick was the fault of the vet, but those hairy little demons don't do themselves any favours. They may be cute and cuddly at home, but at work they would make a terrier proud.

However, it is not always our fault when patients don't get better. We have a great saying in the surgery: 'It is not what you say that matters, but what the client hears'. Explaining things to clients properly is one of the most important things that we ever do.

Take, for example, the Clements' poor spaniel, who had a terrible ear infection. Their dog had been shaking its ear for a couple of weeks before they came into the surgery one evening. The smell from the ear was overpowering and I was surprised they had not come in earlier. I stood the little dog on the table and cleaned his ears out, removing the bulk of the wax and infection. It was so bad that it would need not only ear ointment but also antibiotic tablets. I sent them home with instructions that they were to give their dog ointment in the ears both morning and evening, and antibiotics, one tablet twice daily. If they were worried, they were to give me a ring. Well, like the dog, I heard nothing for a couple of days, so I assumed all was going well. Then, on the third day, they rang. They told me things were not going well at all.

"Why, what exactly is happening?" I asked.

"Well, he's shaking his head worse than ever and seems pretty miserable." They drifted off into a plaintive sort of silence on the phone. The kind when you know they are trying to find the right words.

"It's just that … well … not only that, there is just no way we can get any more of those tablets into his ear. His ears are stuffed full."

"Ah," I replied, and took a deep breath.

Next time, I declared to my staff, I must make sure that I am much clearer in any instructions I give. I got them to bring the dog straight down; the poor thing looked like a novelty pill box. We gave him a sedative and carefully removed six large palatable antibiotic tablets from his ears. He must have been in agony. In their eyes it was my fault, and to be honest they were only following my instructions to the letter. As they pointed out to me, I hadn't said the tablets needed to be given by mouth. These were intelligent people, but when it came to treating animals I was responsible, so I had to apologise.

Actually some owners never cease to surprise me, and Barbie's owners were no exception. Barbie was a lucky dog. She was a very lucky dog. She was a middle-aged basset and, as a rule, bassets are quite the stationary chaps and chapesses. They're not the wandering types. So it was strange that she had decided to trundle off down the lane to explore and found a ruddy big main road and a high speed car racing towards her. What some might consider a design fault of the basset actually saved her life. They're not very high off the ground, i.e. short (I think the politically correct term is vertically challenged). So the bulk of her went under the car. And being fundamentally tubular in shape, she rolled and bounced. Not very dignified, but at least having an odd shape, and gravity on her side, she didn't take off in a short canine flight and break lots of bones. She had, however, still managed to make quite a mess of herself.

She was bleeding heavily from her mouth and was unable to walk. Her owner and mum, Donna Sellers, gently carried her into the surgery. The Sellers are tough people. He runs a demolition business and she runs the paperwork side of it. They were not the sort of people you would expect to care about their pets, but never judge a book by its cover. The

Sellers are typical British animal lovers. I can tell you that they are truly delightful people when it comes to their pets. They were absolutely distraught when they brought Barbie in; you really would have thought that the world had coming crashing down.

Izzie wasn't there at the time, which was probably just as well as I am not sure we could have ever shown Barbie on TV, her injuries were so horrific. They placed her on the table and it was obvious that we would have to act quickly if we were to save her life. We admitted her and put her onto a drip. This was to try and raise her blood pressure because she was in shock, and we were also unsure how much blood she had lost. She was given painkillers and antibiotics in the drip, and this sent her off into a woozy haze. With her more comfortable, and in a world of her own, we could now set about looking at her more closely.

Immediately obvious was the mess her face was in. Her jaw was hanging at an unusual angle and the rest of her face a mask of blood; pretty gory, but, on closer inspection, it wasn't as bad as it seemed. Her skull seemed fairly intact and both eyes looked dim but clear. There didn't appear to be any major brain injury either, so we allowed ourselves to be cautiously hopeful. The next obvious thing was that her left leg was positioned at a rather odd angle. It was badly broken too and would need fixing.

Barbie was kept sedated and on strong painkillers and a drip for several days whilst we allowed her to get over the initial shock of the road traffic accident. She was a remarkably strong little dog, and as each day passed she impressed me with her fighting spirit. Her owners had obviously imprinted their intelligence and survival instinct upon her.

Once we'd cleaned her up thoroughly, apart from the jaw and leg, there were no other visible injuries. In fact, by the third day she was looking almost perky, apart from the rather revolting sight of her mangled jaw hanging down (but hey, if I'd been hit by a car I'd be down in the mouth), (sorry). Izzie decided that this would now be a good case to film, and the owners were such pleasant people it would be a shame to miss it.

The next task was to fix the bones. The jaw seemed the worst, so I decided to fix that first. There was no way we were going to be able to do both operations in one go, it would all be too much for Barbie, so I decided to separate the operations by a few days.

Modern orthopaedic surgery is very advanced and, on the whole, most fractured bones can be repaired these days. Barbie's jaw was no exception. The mandible had broken in three places and it would all need to be lined up correctly if her mouth was to open and close properly and allow her to eat.

Izzie filmed whilst I anaesthetised Barbie and X-rayed the jaw. We needed to know exactly how bad the fractures were if we were going to be able to put it all back together. As always with Barbie, it wasn't as bad as it looked, the worst bit being the ends of the bone sticking out through the gum. This made infection a real problem. But, jaw bone is very resilient and seems to have amazing self-healing properties. Because the pieces were infected, I decided that the most sensible way to tackle this would be with external fixation. This would involve drilling long pins into the jaw bone from the outside then joining them together to form a rigid framework. Provided the pieces of jaw were held together firmly, and in approximately the correct alignment, then the bone should knit. Antibiotics were much in evidence to counteract the infection. Although those nasty human super-bugs are creeping into veterinary and causing us problems, they don't seem to have reached Stamford Bridge yet!

I put a total of eight long pins into the jaw to hold it together, and then bent a larger pin to run all the way round the outside to join all these pins together. The operation took a long time and, after two hours, there was no doubt that my decision to operate on her leg another day was a good one. Exhaustion and stress were taking their toll on me more than the dog. We popped her back into the kennel and covered her in blankets to keep her warm. The next few days should tell. With her jaw fixed, I was hoping that she would be able to eat soft food again pretty soon. This would help build her strength up and give her a good footing on the road to recovery.

The following morning she amazed me even more. She was up, wagging her tail and looking quite the perky pooch. She was still holding one leg up in the air, that still had to be fixed, but, by jove, that dog had spirit. I opened a tin of liquid food, a strong mixture of chicken and rice, with lots of carbohydrates. If we could get her eating this, half the battle would be won. I don't really know what I was fussing about; she happily licked it all off my finger.

The next job was to operate on the leg. I was still unsure exactly what injuries she had sustained here, and I was only going to find out when I had her asleep again. So two days later we re-anaesthetised her.

The X-rays of the leg showed that she had broken it in two places. She had managed to knock the tip off her shoulder blade, so this would need to be fixed back into place with a small screw. She had also smashed her elbow. Both of these injuries are common, though perhaps not both at the same time.

It didn't take long to put all the right bones back into their correct places and fix them there with a variety of screws and pins. Barbie was finally all back together, albeit looking like an Ikea drawer unit that had been assembled without the instructions. The rather odd metal framework around her head was bizarre, like something from an early episode of *Dr Who*, but necessary and, thankfully, temporary.

It was time she went home, so I rang Donna to come in and pick her up. She came down with John her husband, and the look of happiness on their faces is what being a vet is all about. I was going to add a little joke about keeping her away from magnets, and them being able to get Radio 4 now, but I decided against it.

Barbie went home, and over the next two months her owners stayed with her day and night, hand-feeding her small bits at a time of liquid food and then slowly moving her onto more solid food. Once a week they brought her in for me to check, and the improvement each time was amazing. After a couple of months we had to re-anaesthetise her again, to remove all the metal work. She was a completely different dog by now, and was hard to anaesthetise because she didn't really want to stay still on the operating table. I don't really blame her, as I suspect she had rather strong memories of the last time she was there. With the metal rigging all off, she looked almost normal. Her mouth had healed well and she was no longer limping on her right forelimb. I was very pleased, and even more pleased that we had managed to catch such a happy story on camera. Barbie and the Sellers were a big hit when that series went out. But, with everything healed up, I didn't see much of them again for ages.

When I finally decided to move the surgery to new premises, John Sellers was one of the first people I thought of to help.

He was, after all, in the demolition business and was just the kind of man I needed. I had been looking for a new site for ages, but it hadn't been easy. Up until now the surgery had been in a building attached to Stuart and Pauline's house. They had kindly agreed to our staying there for three years after he retired, but we would need to find somewhere new when they wanted their house back.

The main requirements for our new site were that it needed to be in Stamford Bridge, be large enough, and have plenty of space for parking. That old cliché of 'location, location, location' is so true, particularly with a vet's practice.

Time was flying by, and I realised that I needed to find somewhere fast because it also had to be built. I was fortunate that just adjacent to the Bridge was an old disused clothes shop. This had been boarded up and derelict for years, ever since the bad floods of 1999 and 2000. Since then, with government money, the council had built a large flood defence wall to protect the site. This place would be ideal. I went to see the owners one afternoon to see if they would be willing to part with the land. As they opened the door and saw me, they immediately said:

"We know why you've come, and the answer is yes."

How about that for lucky; I hadn't even said a word.

Poor old Izzie though; she was trying to film, and I had just embarked upon building a brand new veterinary surgery. Now she not only had to manage all the filming, but a stressed vet as well. However, she rose to the occasion. She took to looking at me carefully to see if I was in a caring-veterinary frame of mind or a hard-nosed no-nonsense building controller one. If I was in the wrong one, she would either disappear or quietly remind me what I should be doing.

The first job was obviously to design a surgery. Over the next few months, Diana and I drove round the countryside looking at vet surgeries, and gleaning useful tips from each one. Finally I sketched out my plans and took them along to an architect. I gave him the remit to design me a surgery but under no circumstances was he to change my floor layout of the downstairs. Poor fellow; I suspect it is the architect's equivalent of having to neuter a dog but without making a cut in the skin.

As he drew more and more complicated designs, I would go in and admire them and sadly tell him that they were beyond the reach of my budget. So the plans would shrink again. It must be very frustrating being an architect. Half way through the design process, the plans underwent a massive hiccup when a friend saw them and suggested building the upstairs from wood. This was a great idea. To use a sustainable resource that was almost carbon neutral appealed to every one in the surgery. We could have a 'state of the art' vet surgery downstairs and a cosy 'log cabin-like office complex' upstairs. I did, however, reject my nurses' ideas about wood-burning stoves and deep thick rugs. I had to: it would have escalated into steam rooms and a ski-lift knowing my lot! Luckily for me, my friend imported these types of buildings from Finland.

The first thing to do was to demolish the old clothes shop, and this was where John Sellers came in. The planning permission had only just come through the post when John levelled the lot. I think he enjoyed finding a way to help after all the work we had done on Barbie the previous year. And his job must be one of the most satisfying on the planet!

After this, the surgery went up quickly. Work started in March and we had moved in by November. We used builders, electricians and plumbers who had looked after us for years, so I knew I could count on them. I also knew their wives, so when they didn't turn up (as builders seem to instinctively do) I could always ring their homes and grass them up; this always did the trick. Much to the amusement of the builders, Izzie filmed the erection of our mega building and the many laughs we had doing it (amazingly the joke about my new erection never wore thin, but you had to be there). But in the end, as the programme was meant to be about vets, rather than grand designs, most of it was edited out. I did ask that they broadcast the grand opening, and Ali agreed. It was only right and proper that we should end that particular series with the grand opening of the Ark, our new surgery. It all fitted in rather well.

Chapter Twenty-eight

2006 was a great year in many other ways, as we finally managed to find a replacement for Rosie. We had all missed the squawking company that a parrot can bring to a house. And even though cockatoos really are the noisiest of all parrots, her absence was grimly underlined by the ominous silence in the house. Steve had the answer.

Steve is a terribly nice bloke, dedicated in the extreme. He runs the National Parrot Sanctuary. This is a much-needed site of refuge for the enormous numbers of parrots that outlive their stay in private homes. Most parrots really don't make good pets. They are, after all, wild animals that happen to have been fairly well socialised and imprinted on humans. However, as they grow up and become sexually mature, they often become confused as to whether they are human or a parrot. When they start pulling their feathers out or destroying the house, in frustration or boredom, they seem to end up being thrown out or at Steve's in a bad shape (a polygon, even: geddit?).

At any one time Steve has more than 1000 of them! Imagine the cacophony that little lot make!

They are kept in large groups of conspecifics, i.e. groups of the same species. In some aviaries, he has nearly 150 flying together in a group. This so closely mimics their natural behaviour that many of them revert to being wild parrots. Some, however, are so imprinted and so friendly that they will never be able to return to being wild. One such is Jojo. When I went to visit Steve to look at some of his other parrots, he asked me about Rosie. I explained how she had burnt herself badly and finally ended up dying. He told me he had just the thing for me, an umbrella cockatoo called Jojo.

Jojo was an adult rescue bird that Steve had had in for several months. She was so friendly that there was just no possibility of her mixing with the other parrots, making her just right for us. A few weeks later Clare went down and collected her. She quickly became a member of the Brash Street Kids, as we call ourselves.

She is near as damn it Rosie reincarnated! She happily allows the kids to haul her around and helps out in the garden gently pruning the hedge for us. For when we're all out, we have built her an aviary so she can still be outside watching the world go by. The rest of the time she spends paddling around the house being useful. She loves the computer keyboard and rips all the keys out for fun; she hasn't quite cracked typing just yet.

The same year marked my return to the Malton Show. The Malton Show is an annual event; it's as much as anything a celebration of rural life. It is always held on a Thursday and all the local schools have the day off, allowing the whole family to go. It was, and still is, one of the local highlights of the year. When Izzie asked me if we could go and film at the show, I thought it would be fun but I was also slightly hesitant.

I wasn't entirely sure whether I would be welcome. You see, many years earlier, I had been told off by the committee for potentially bringing the show into disrepute. Over a loaf of bread.

Let me explain. The show has competitions in almost everything. There are the normal cattle, sheep and poultry competitions, hotly contested with incredibly well manicured beasts. Far more fun, in my opinion, are the vast tents stuffed full with an array of weird and wonderful pigeons and chickens. In these tents you can lose yourself for hours trying to guess the names of the different breeds. In other large tents are the competitions for home produce and, tucked away in one corner, is the 'One Pound White Loaf' competition.

A long time ago, and I'm not saying that I'm proud of my actions, but it was fun, a group of young farmers, a cartoonist and myself decided to enter the One Pound White Loaf competition. I mean, how hard can baking be? I felt confident my entry would win and be the talk of the show for many years to come. And in a way it was.

There was normally only a smattering of entries for this competition so, after a lot of gastronomic bravado, my friends and I decided we would all enter, and may the best loaf win. Mine, of course.

Approximately one month before the show we all met one evening at the pub. The first thing to decide were the exact rules that we would play under. Obviously, practising making the bread could not be allowed. That would be cheating. Similarly, purchasing a loaf or getting any assistance from anyone who had the vaguest idea of what they were doing would also not be in the spirit of the game.

We would have to get up at five a.m. on the morning of the show and each cook a freshly baked one pound white loaf from scratch. The final rule was that whatever we made would have to be entered; there was to be no retreat! Even if our loaves looked like something that had crawled off *The Island of Dr Moreau*, we would still enter them. At our initial meeting there were just three of us, but the numbers very quickly grew until finally there were about seven of us who were going to enter. We genuinely felt that the Malton Show would be chuffed to bits to have their bread competition elevated to such new heights of competitiveness.

To celebrate our miniature competition, we had made a small trophy. A slice of white bread had been soaked in linseed oil, and then baked hard. It was then mounted on a piece of wire and then on a plinth and looked a rather dashing first prize.

On the day in question, I was up early. Before going to bed I had laid out everything that was needed, and even found a recipe! Although I do enjoy cooking, making bread was not something I had done very often, and it was normally with slightly mixed results.

I mixed my yeast with warm water, and put it on the back of the Aga to do its stuff. I mixed the gooey frothy mixture with the flour and everything else required. I set my loaf to rise and had tea. This was going fine, I thought. An hour later, when the loaf was looking much larger, I popped it into the oven for half an hour. Once the half hour was up, I brought my masterpiece out of the Aga. It smelt fabulous, but sadly a large crack had appeared across the top, making it look slightly unsightly, but I decided to call its look 'organic', i.e. natural. Besides, there was no time to worry about it. It was my entry and that was that. I rushed off to the show to drop it in before the deadline of nine o'clock.

Perhaps the look of disgust on the judges' faces should have told me that they really were not impressed, but this was my beautiful baby, my bun from my oven, and I loved it and didn't care what anyone said about it! Of our seven entries, each one of us admitted to having the same feelings of pride about our loaves and thoroughly expected to take home the prize for our wonderful creations.

Of course, this didn't happen, because the judges hadn't gone through the wonderful emotions we'd all gone through baking our first loaves, and saw them for what they really were: utter rubbish. We began to see this too. Seven of the most twisted, molested, burned, scorched and downright ugly loaves of bread you have ever seen. One judge described them all as a shameful waste of flour. We managed to persuade another judge to place Jamie's, the very least deformed, as number five, so he came first in our private competition.

"Oh well," I mused, "there's always next year."

"Don't threaten me," said a judge.

This private competition of ours carried on for a number of years, but none of us ever took home the real prize. There was obviously considerably more to this competition than meets the eye. I think the final straw that broke the camel's back was the year of 1997. It was our fifth year of entering. I still had not managed to win the coveted trophy, but felt that this year was my year. After my first over-the-top loaf, I had dropped the levels of yeast, and for several years had been producing loaves that were either medieval in design or would have been better employed in a builder's yard propping something up. This year I decided to cheat.

I practised. I admit it was wrong, but the competitive streak in me was coming out, and I really wanted to win. Then I decided to cook two loaves at the same time, so I could enter the best one.

I got up early and prepared my loaves. I popped the first in the oven and, after a short while, it was ready. It looked perfect, almost shop bought. It had risen to perfection, was lightly brown on the top and sounded hollow when I tapped it on the bottom. The second one went just as well. As I then had a spare loaf, to check they were OK inside, I cut the first one open. Perfect. My cheating plan was working! This year I would definitely be placed. My brother-in-law had joined the competition by now and, if nothing else, I had to ensure that I beat him.

When I went along later that day with the family, I quickly went over to the home produce tent to see how I had done. It was important to remain fairly incognito when looking at our loaves, or we could get pulled in by the judges. To ensure anonymity, the loaves are only numbered, but I knew which was mine so would be able to pick it out.

As part of the judging process, the loaves are cut in half to check the consistency and bubbles inside. This is what let my loaf down. Although it looked perfect on the outside, risen, brown and well shaped, within the middle was a soup of still-liquid dough. There on the table it sat, with its insides gently flowing out, looking like a battle-damaged dalek. I was gutted. I slunk off quietly, knowing that my entry would once again not win.

Unfortunately the Malton Show had decided they had had enough of this amateurish behaviour, and a half-arsed entry of a half-cooked loaf was just taking the mickey. In the post the following day I received a letter advising me that perhaps it would be best all round if I did not enter the competition. Well, I didn't want to poke fun at all the hard work the people who genuinely entered the competition had put in, and so agreed the only thing I could do was to withdraw. No, that's not true:

what I really wanted to do was bake a batch of rock cakes and take the judges' greenhouse windows out, but I soon calmed down and thankfully didn't do anything of the sort. Besides, it could have escalated and I might have been found knee-capped by the WI in a ditch somewhere as a result of a reprisal attack.

So, when a falconer asked me to drop in to the Show to inspect some birds of prey, I wasn't terribly sure I would be welcome. Luckily, Malton Show is a much bigger show than that, and fortunately had long since forgotten the follies of my youth.

The falconer was going to use his birds in a show in which he would display his control over these wild, free-minded, hunter-killers. Izzie was going to film me checking the birds, and then his display. One of the birds had a slight lesion on its claw, but I said it was fine to take part in the display; I was happy with the birds. I was less enamoured with the Yorkshire weather, though. It went from grim to 'orrible and a gale force wind was blowing up. The falconer assured me his control over the birds would ensure they'd be OK in the elements, and the dark foreboding sky would add to the ambience, as would his medieval costume. The man's a fool, I thought.

He took centre stage in the great ring, and the crowd gathered around him. Speaking to them over his radio-microphone, he explained all about falconry, launched the birds, and began his display of aeronautical avian dexterity. He lost the first bird straight away. A huge gust of wind disorientated it and it ended up in Scarborough, miles away. This sadly brought the display to a quick ending. He'd had the foresight to tag the birds with radio-transmitters, and was running around in a blind panic, holding what looked like an old-style TV aerial, desperate to get a fix. However, even by driving his van and hanging out of the window with the aerial in his hand, barking the bird's name out, he still couldn't find it. It took six hours to establish a radio fix, but the frightened, distressed creature was finally reunited with his hawk, which had had a nice day out in Scarborough. I felt sorry for the poor man after all his hard work in preparing for the Show. But then I also knew that not everything always goes according to plan at the Malton Show.

Chapter Twenty-nine

As a vet I should never have a bad word to say about any living creature, and usually I don't. Well, apart from Nelson the chimp, with whom I have always had a rather rocky relationship.

But I must confess to having a bit of a dread about insects and spiders. They're creepy, they're crawly and they make weird sounds. Doubtless they have a similar opinion of us, but we're the big 'uns, so what are they going to do?

Joking aside, why do we humans have an inbuilt dread of most insects? Is it because they're so different? Perhaps. But aren't frogs, for example, incredibly different from us too? Yet they're revered as cute and amusing. Maybe if Kermit the Frog had been Kermit the Cockroach, with the same joyful personality, we'd have gone to bed as kids cuddling cute fluffy toy cockroaches. Perhaps Pooh Bear should have been Pooh Dung Beetle. Then we wouldn't have this negative view of insects.

Perhaps a lot of my negativity stems from my upbringing abroad. My parents were in the Foreign Office, so I was brought up in many parts of the world, including the Far East. I have strong memories of seeing bird-eating spiders sitting on telegraph lines patiently waiting to fall on unsuspecting birds (and me) below. Hideous. This would stop me walking under those wires, which occasionally meant long detours. But I was only seven and, with hindsight, it is quite possible that most of those spiders were actually the birds. There did seem to be rather a lot of them. Since then, I have tried to steer clear of things with more than four legs. They certainly never entered the syllabus at college.

However, having qualified, as the junior assistant this sort of creature was exactly what I was meant to deal with, partners being far too busy. I had only been out of college for a couple of weeks when I had to face my first many-legged patient.

Your average A&E department is always ready for a plethora of bikers waiting to be stitched and bandaged up after a short, sharp lesson in 'two wheels good, four wheels better'. But your average, common-or-garden, vet? Surely not. But, what else was I to expect when a burly biker strode into the surgery saying:

"It's Harold, he's bleeding to death!"

He was hard to understand because he was wearing a crash helmet and was almost in tears with despair. I half expected an entourage of Hell's Angels to walk in carrying one of their number on a stretcher, and I was groping for ways of telling them I was just a little old vet who didn't 'do humans', so please don't hit me.

The large biker took off his helmet and repeated his statement about 'Harold'. He said Harold was outside on the back of his bike, in a box. Oh dear, I thought, it sounds like it might be a bit late for him anyway! When he brought Harold in, I was relieved to see he was in fact a red-kneed tarantula.

I say relieved, but this was relative. This was a large spider, with big hairy legs, and long sharp-looking fangs. The sort you see in *Lord of the Rings*. But the poor eight-legged chap was indeed losing fluid; a clear liquid called endolymph was oozing from a crack in his endoskeleton. Harold was bleeding to death, and I was a vet.

"How did this happen?" I asked, as my imagination ran wild with thoughts of Harold perched on a Harley Davidson's handlebars as he and the biker were 'Moving on the Queen's Highway looking like a streak of lightning!', to quote Chris Spedding in his 70s song Motorbiking (now I'm showing my age). Or maybe there'd been a rumpus between rival Hell's Angels and Harold had taken a bike chain across the back in the debacle!

"I was cuddling him when I dropped him," said the biker.

"Oh," I said, rather anticlimactically.

Apparently the biker cuddled Harold every night and shared a pint of beer with him. A joke about how long it takes to get a spider legless popped into my head, but thankfully stayed there. Besides, I was judging this tough-looking chap and had no right to. He was obviously a keen animal lover and understandably upset about his pet.

An idea sprang to mind. I couldn't sew the endoskeleton back together, but I could glue it! I found a tube of Superglue, pushed the crack together and applied two liberal drops of the cosmic adhesive and waited for the wound to set.

"There we go," I said, "not the neatest cosmetic surgery, I grant you, but it'll hold until he next sheds his skin and he'll be back to normal."

The biker looked amazed and befuddled. "It's really that simple?" he asked.

I nodded, and off the biker roared. I often wonder if I put a dangerous thought into his head that day. Did he think this was a miracle solve-all method? I had terrible thoughts about hordes of Hell's Angels charging about the countryside without a care for their own safety because they all had copious tubes of Superglue in their leather jacket pockets. However, I was secretly very proud of myself; I had put my creepy-crawlie bigotry behind me and managed to treat a spider.

I had very few dealings with any sort of insect or spider for years after that, except of course the ubiquitous fleas and ticks. Fleas are certainly the most common cause of irritations we see in dogs and cats, and they can be extremely difficult to get rid of, particularly once they have established a hold in a house. In multi-animal houses, it is often a lost cause.

Mrs McIntosh and her dogs was one such case. Mrs Mac, as she was affectionately known, was a large lady, a very large lady. She had to weigh at least 15 stone, but she had a heart to match and loved her dogs with a passion. She ran a trout fishery with her husband, and had been kind enough to always allow me to try my rather feeble fly-fishing attempts in their pond, so I knew the dogs well. They started with Charlie, the large Great Dane, and moved down in size through a German Shepherd, a Springer spaniel, a terrier and finally ended with Minnie, the dachshund. All of them were much loved and led a riotous and slightly chaotic life around the trout fishery. Manners were perhaps not high on their minds, sometimes a bit like my four boys.

As a result of this outward-bound lifestyle, they had diseases to fit, and the greatest of their problems was their fleas. They were heaving in fleas. Treating them was difficult, as Mrs Mac was extremely allergic to all the sprays, spot-ons and shampoos, that we had ever tried. Finally one summer, the problem got too much for her, and she arrived at the surgery demanding action. Once again I patiently explained that there was little else I could offer, except the standard armoury of drugs that we had on our shelves. But then an idea came to me. I remembered reading somewhere that a lot of wild animals will use bathing as a method of decreasing the numbers of ectoparasites carried in their coats, and this might help. But it was not just an ordinary bath I was suggesting; it was a bath in the sea.

"The only thing I can suggest that you do is to try taking them for a swim in the sea. The fleas hate salt water, and it should help."

Well, it was summer time and, being a hot sunny day, she headed straight off for the beach. The plan perhaps broke down slightly in that she didn't discuss it with her dogs. On arriving at the beach in Filey, she decamped all the dogs from her car, and walked down to the beach.

"In," she shouted, "in!"

The dogs stared at her as if she was mad. They had not played this game before, and anyway who was 'In'? But she was a determined woman, and had not driven all that way for nothing; so undeterred, she grasped the first dog to hand, picked up Minnie in her other arm, and waded out to sea fully clothed. Once a suitable distance out from the shore, and remember it shelves very shallowly here, so she would have had to go a fair way out, she dumped the dogs in the sea. She then turned and waded back to the shore. At the shore, the three remaining dogs watched in mild amusement, whilst out at sea the other two headed back to the shore. At this point, a small crowd of people formed to watch this rather unusual spectacle. A large 15-stone lady, fully clothed, dragging her dogs one by one, unwilling, into the sea. By the time she had returned to start grappling with her Great Dane, the police had arrived. Concerned onlookers were convinced that she had lost the plot and was now trying to drown her clan.

"I assure you I am not," she replied to their questioning, "I am acting purely on my vet's orders!"

Although in some ways I have always wished that the cameras had been there to catch it all on film, I was relieved they weren't when the inspector turned up to corroborate her story. As he took my statement, I could see that the RSPCA and the Royal College of Veterinary Surgeons were going to take a dim view; perhaps this was going to be the end of my career.

Because I corroborated her story, that luckily seemed to be the end of the matter, and no charges were ever brought. Besides it had worked, and for a good few weeks the flea problem died down. Though I have to say I am not advocating throwing one's dog into the sea as a first line of treatment for fleas. If you do plan to use this method of control, then you should certainly only do it if you have your dogs on board.

There is one other particularly memorable time that ectoparasites and I crossed paths. Sadly, as with many of these more amusing occasions, the camera wasn't there. This was the time when the Lorraines rang in a panic one morning. They had been out walking their dog, and on their return they had cleaned all the mud off the dog. Whilst doing so, they had noticed a large number of ticks on the dog's tummy.

We made an appointment for them to come in later that day, but this they ignored. Convinced that if they waited too long their dog would die from blood loss, they came charging straight down.

On arrival they overruled my nurse and insisted on being seen immediately. By now I began to feel concerned that maybe there was actually something pretty seriously wrong with their little dog, so I stopped what I was doing and went out to the consulting room to meet them.

They explained that they had been on the moors and had found enormous numbers of ticks when they were cleaning their much beloved dog afterwards. I was ready for the worst, but when I ran my hand under the dog's tummy I could feel nothing.

"I can't feel anything," I said.

"You're wrong. She's heaving in ticks," they insisted.

We turned her over, and they pointed out the long line of ticks. In fact, there were two lines, running parallel down either side of the dog's undercarriage.

"Those are nipples," I said, as gently as I could.

"Are you sure?" came back the reply.

It took confirmation from my colleague and one of the nurses for them to believe me, and even so they left muttering under their breath that the nipples hadn't been there before the walk. Somehow, sometimes, we can never please all of our clients all of the time.

Even though I spend a lot of time dealing with small bugs like ticks and fleas, I was still alarmed when Flamingo Land decided they were to open an insectarium. The aquarium had recently been moved underneath the sea lion's pad, so there was this large, dark room ready for something unearthly to move in. The Zoo management decided that it would be perfect to house creepy-crawlies in. I am sure they were right, but was unsure I wanted to be the creepy-crawlies' vet.

The first tenants were the cockroaches, and the keeper, Dean, who was to run this den of thoraxes and feelers, brought in two boxes, each containing ten hissing creatures of the Order Blattodea. Ten female, ten male, but they looked identical to me.

I opened the lids and took a long, hard look at these two-inch long insects. Flat, broad and tough looking, with long waving antennae. Dean asked me to start putting the females into their new tank while he put the males in. I took a deep breath and dubiously picked one out of the second box. It hissed at me, which was unnerving. I glanced over at Dean. He too was being hissed at but wasn't fazed at all. I was impressed by his knowledge of these enigmatic creatures, and asked him how he could so easily identify which were the males and which were the females. He looked at me blankly and pointed to the boxes.

"It says on the lids."

I pretty soon got used to the cockroaches; they're alright as it happens, they just get bad press. They're just trying to get along, after all. As are most insects. Dean talks to his insects as though they are any other animal, and keeps them happy and depression free. Insect keepers live by the motto, 'Don't get caught with your flies down'.

Then again, the bigger the insect, the more getting used to they take. Tarantulas are notoriously creepy.

The insectarium was filling up 'nicely', and Dean rang me to say he was taking in his first tarantula and could I come and give it the once over. I was apprehensive, and told him that if he checked it had somewhere between seven and nine legs it would probably be OK. He labelled me a wuss and told me to get over there.

Quick as a flash, I finished the book I was reading, and took a leisurely drive over to the Zoo. It was a Mexican tarantula, so before I took it out of its travel case I tried to imagine it with a little sombrero on, to make it cuter. I tipped its box on its side and waited for it to appear. Izzie was filming, enjoying every moment of my fear.

Slowly, a long black hairy leg appeared from the bedding. Dean advised me to hold out my hand so that the spider could walk calmly onto my palm. I did so, and the whole bloody thing flopped out of the box in one short thud, landing on my hand. And in the best traditions of a certain Miss Muffet, I yelped like a little girl and was very nearly frightened away.

I admit I was temporarily frozen with terror, but it very soon subsided. It was actually quite relaxing feeling the tarantula walking on my hand. They're affectionate creatures, ask any owner, and make great companions. They just look weird!

A good way to tell if a tarantula is happy or not is to check if it's bald. Honest! When a tarantula is unhappy it sheds the small, fine hairs on the back of its abdomen. In the tarantula world, hairy is happy.

If I haven't convinced you of the worthiness of creepy-crawlies then you might want to think about owning a squirrel monkey. These have the opposite effect, and will happily rid your house of every little bug that moves. I once went to inspect a couple of monkeys a sweet lady owned, solely because they kept the house totally insect and spider free. The downside to owning a squirrel monkey is that they are potentially dangerous to humans and require a DWA licence, rather like the gilamonsters.

This lady did indeed live in an immaculate house: not a fly, spider or wasp anywhere to be seen. She let the monkeys out of their cage and they leapt on her, cuddling her with the greatest, most heart-warming affection. I commented on how much they adored her, and with a flush of humble pride she told me they loved her for her singing. Apparently she sang in nightclubs and the spider monkeys were her biggest fans. Driving home, I imagined her vacuuming the house as her two furry little fans sat on the sofa, arm in arm, listening to her. Maybe even humming away in simian harmony. Then I thought about what she said: did she mean she took them to the nightclubs with her!? That'd be a great act if she did. She could claim her backing group was The Monkeys!

Chapter Thirty

This, I think, is the last chapter. I'm relieved about this because, as Quentin Crisp once said at the end of an interview, 'You must stop this ... now as I have come to the end of my personality'.

I feel the same way. Plus it's taken a hell of a long time. I've never written a book before; I've coloured a few in, but never actually sat down and written one. It was fun, though, and a lot of wonderful, enjoyable memories have been reborn in these pages. However, at the time of writing, we've been filming another series of *Zoo Vet* and I think it's all been a bit frustrating for Izzie. She can handle my stressed-out days regarding clients, animals, moving surgery, etc., but the strain of writing a book about my life is an extravagance I've brought on myself.

The series of *Zoo Vet* that we have just finished shooting is, as always, the best yet. Izzie, like Katie before her, just gets better and better. It certainly has some of the loveliest stories in it that I think we have ever shot. For example, the delivery of the new-born giraffe contrasts marvellously with the problems I had trying to take a blood sample from the rhinos.

I would like to think that over the eight years we have been filming at the Zoo we have managed not only to teach a little about the weird and wonderful animals that are kept there, but also how much care and attention goes into looking after them behind the scenes. Zoos sometimes get a lot of bad press. If that is well deserved, well then fair enough, but in most cases, and certainly with our Zoo, this is not the case. The animals at Flamingo Land are carefully tended and nurtured. You'd be hard put to find somewhere else that does it better. It's a hotel for animals, and I don't just mean a 'travel tavern', I'm talking the Ritz. Has to be! Zoos are closely inspected by an independent governing body, just like schools have Ofsted. And the owners of a good zoo know that healthier, happier animals make for better attractions.

Flamingo Land continues to go from strength to strength, and I feel lucky to be part of that. It hasn't always been easy, and I have certainly been kept on my toes. Four years ago I had to go back to the books to pass another type of degree so that I could keep up-to-date with the knowledge that I need. As a friend once said to me, 'Trying to be an up-to-date zoo vet is like trying to treat a lively hamster, you're never going to grasp all of it at once'. The volume of information out there just grows exponentially.

I have been asked many questions over the years of filming. Often they're quite gruesome, and sometimes they're just daft.

"Do you treat wasps?"

"No I don't, what gave you that idea?"

"I saw one in your waiting room."

But two questions I am often asked have the same answer.

"What's your favourite animal?"

"Tiggy the tapir."

"What's your favourite bit of film?"

"Tiggy the tapir."

This piece of filming was of Tiggy when she gave birth. Or at least tried to.

Tiggy lives with Woody. These two quiet South American tapirs live in a wooded bit of the Zoo at the end of the bird walk. I remember when Woody first arrived. He was a grumpy old so-and-so and, although he would let the keepers handle him, back then I could never get anywhere near. Over the years, as the keepers have played with him more and more, he has become ever-more chilled and nowadays he is so relaxed you can pretty well do anything you like. And that includes the vet. This, for me, is a real treat, because, as you now know, almost all the animals at the Zoo just don't like me. Heck, most of them want my head mounted on their cage walls.

Despite all the injections that I have now given the tapirs, they don't seem to care. All they really want in the world is a good scratch and tickle. They are so laid back that when you go in there and start tickling their flanks, they just flop over on their backs and ask for more.

I would add a word of caution, however; they do have ferocious teeth and, Woody in particular, can get somewhat sex crazed. He has bitten poor old Tiggy several times when he was feeling horny, and left us treating some nasty holes in her. I guess this is just their nature; I'm just glad I'm not his type!

Tiggy and Woody have successfully bred just the once. Their offspring went off to a different zoo when he was big enough to join another breeding group. These are fairly rare animals, whose habitat in the wild seems to be disappearing fast, so any chance to enable them to reproduce is taken. We knew ours had mated again and we were expecting a new tapir any day when Sam rang one morning to say that Tiggy wasn't well.

Her udder had been bagged up for about a week, a sure sign that birth was imminent. That morning she had suddenly gone off colour.

On arrival, I went to look at her. She normally gets up off the straw and comes over to say hello before flopping over for the customary tickle. On this particular morning she didn't want any of it, and just lay there. The look in her eyes told me she was completely fed up. I worked my way round to the back end, looking closely at her, tickling all the time. Although she was relaxed, I had to bear in mind she was a wild animal in discomfort and a wrong move in the wrong sore place might result in a savage nip and a fortnight for me in intensive care.

Mind you, she seemed to be feeling so rotten I think she was past caring. When I reached her vagina I noticed a tiny bloody discharge. She was giving birth, or at least trying to.

I needed to feel inside, but was unsure how she was going to react to this. Tapirs are such round little animals that any other sort of examination from the outside is pretty well useless.

I stripped off, not to look good on camera, my days for that have long gone, but to avoid getting too much muck all over my new shirt. After liberally applying lots of obstetric jelly over my arm, I bent down to try and have a feel inside. What I didn't want to do was to have Tiggy get up and lose her temper just when I was up to my shoulder inside her. This would be difficult to explain to her, and I could end up with an arm in there to remove as well as a baby Tiggy. I could just imagine the tabloid image of me, arm deep in a tapir, half-naked, in mid-air with the rest of the staff pulling on my feet to get me out. The headline would have read 'I'm a TV Vet Get Me Out of Tapir!'

We had got Woody out of the way, and he was snuffling and grunting on the other side of the door, wondering who was interfering with his girlfriend. That could be difficult to explain as well.

Tiggy wasn't well at all, and she allowed me to slip my hand into her vagina. Then my forearm, and finally my whole arm. Wow, she was long. She was definitely losing the baby. Her cervix was fully dilated, but the baby seemed to be stuck. I could feel two paws, but nothing else. There was little chance of it coming out on its own, as the whole lot had dried out. Sadly the foetus was obviously dead and beginning to rot. Unless we got it out, Tiggy would certainly die. I withdrew my arm and had a think. In some ways I was lucky. She was so ill that it had been easy to do everything that I had so far, but I needed to be careful not to push my luck.

I wanted to give her a chance to expel the foetus on her own, so decided to pump a lot of lubricant into her. We carry pumps and long flexible tubes with us in the car, and they would be ideal to get liquid into the uterus (womb). We normally use them in horses with colic. After mixing up obstetric jelly and hot water, it was an easy job to introduce the tube into her uterus and then to pump in 20 litres of the warm solution. With a bit of luck, it would work its way round the rotten foetus, lubricating it sufficiently so that she would be able to push it out. Finally I gave her some antibiotics and an anti-inflammatory to help make her feel a bit better. An epidural was out of the question: I needed her to push. There was so little reaction to the large needle and the 20 cubic centimetres of drugs pumped into her, I had to check she was still with us!

Izzie and I left her and Sam alone for the night, with the promise that we would be back in the morning. If she hadn't managed to get it out on her own, we were facing the possibility of a Caesarean. This was going to be very risky, as she was already a very sick animal.

In the morning she still hadn't produced anything, so I put together my operating kit and headed off to the Zoo with Dawn, one of the nurses. There was no practical way we could ever get many of the bigger Zoo animals to the surgery, so nowadays we have an operating theatre at the Zoo. But even that would be no use in this case; we would never be able to get Tiggy, in her present condition, anywhere near. Any operating we had to do would have to be in her own pen.

Once we had got there, I was pleasantly shocked to see Tiggy was feeling much better! She was up and eating without an apparent care in the world. Of a foetus, however, there was not a sign. She was much harder to examine in her brighter state, and resented me trying to feel inside her. She would have to be knocked out for me to proceed. Normally, of all the animals I deal with, she is the easiest by far, and therefore my favourite. I had thought we might have to dart her, but she just let me walk up to her and inject her. She never moved a muscle. Nelson, if you're reading this, take a leaf out of Tiggy's book, you obstinate old simian!

Whilst we gave her 20 minutes to go to sleep, we were busy. I had brought everything I needed to carry out a Caesarean, including the kitchen sink. It was not an operation I had ever done before on a tapir, so I would have to wing it. The main decision was whether to do a flank incision, as with cows and sheep, or a mid-line one on her tummy, as with cats and dogs. I had spoken to a number of colleagues the night before and, although none of them had done a tapir Caesarean either, mid-line seemed to be the way to go.

Whilst she drifted off to sleep, Dawn and I got ourselves organised. It can be difficult, once you have started, to find things if you're not supremely organised. There is many an instrument that has been lost in the mess of hay and feed whilst carrying out operations in the field. Quite a few patients can be lost too, unless you get your act together.

With Tiggy finally fast asleep, I looked at trying to intubate her. But the long shape of her snout meant that trying to get a tube over her enormous fleshy tongue was going to be impossible, so we settled for putting a face mask on her. This would mean she breathed a mixture of anaesthetic gas and oxygen but, if there were problems, we would not be able to breathe for her.

Next I hooked her up onto a drip, or tried to. Although I could see the veins easily, every time I managed to get a catheter into the vein the vein would blow. By this I mean that it would burst and start bleeding into the surrounding tissues. Tapirs have extremely sensitive veins. This was not going well.

After 15 minutes of faffing about, I left it and decided to have a good feel inside her before moving on to carry out the Caesarean. On plunging my arm into the now gooey, smelly mess, there was good news. All the fluids that I had pumped in overnight had had an effect. The foetus had moved forwards from the uterus into the birth canal, and I was now able to feel two legs. If I could get ropes onto them, and perhaps pull the foetus further, then I might be able to get hold of the head. I might even then get the foetus out without having to resort to risky surgery.

I put ropes onto the two feet and pulled. Nothing happened. This was depressing. I tried again, and there was the slightest movement towards me. Putting down the ropes I had another feel inside. I could now feel the head.

When you have great big hands like mine, I always feel a bit sorry for animals when I have to feel inside them like this. However, they can get their revenge. As I felt inside her, the amount of room was tiny and the walls of her uterus were crushing down on my hand, squeezing it to a pulp. Or at least that's what it felt like.

After about half an hour of struggling, I finally managed to slip a rope over the foetus' head. Now that I had a head and two feet, I should be able to pull it out. I wanted to pump more obstetric jelly in, but we had run out, so I used washing-up liquid mixed with warm water. The old methods still work.

Pulling the foetus out still wasn't easy, and I had to get a keeper to lend a hand. On occasions it felt like we were pulling poor Tiggy backwards along the floor. We had to go carefully; I didn't want to rush this. If we pulled too fast, and the uterus or vagina ripped, then Tiggy could either bleed to death or die from infection at a later date.

Finally, thank goodness, the foetus flopped out onto the floor with a slurping sort of noise. We had got it out.

We were not out of the woods yet, though. Tiggy had been asleep for more than an hour and she hadn't been exactly well before we started. I had a quick feel inside to see that all was OK and that she didn't have twins. She hadn't ripped, so I was hopeful that, if we managed to get her through the anaesthetic, she would live.

We gave her more painkillers and antibiotics and reversed the anaesthetic. We cleared the mass of tools and equipment out of the stable, and sat back and waited to see if she would wake up. The mess of instruments and opened packs outside was a testament to the frenzied activity that had gone on over the preceding hours. Masses of stuff we had brought with us hadn't been needed, but then it is a bit like an umbrella. If we hadn't brought it along, you can bet your bottom dollar we would have needed it.

An hour later Tiggy began to stir. I was worried about her breathing, so we had rolled her over a couple of times so that she used each lung. Slowly but surely she woke up. Although she took ages, she did eventually stand up later that evening.

I turned my attention to the foetus. She had had one live baby before, and this foetus hadn't been presented wrongly, so why had it all gone wrong? I sent the little, perfectly formed but somewhat smelly, foetus off to the Veterinary Investigation Centre in Thirsk. There they could carry out tests to see if there was an answer to our mystery.

The result of their investigation showed that the foetus had died from a bacterial infection and, the foetus being dead, Tiggy had tried to expel it. It was a desperate shame when she had been so near full term in her pregnancy. In the wild she would have died, but we had managed to save her.

Since then both Tiggy and Woody have forgiven me for my intrusion, and Tiggy is, we think, pregnant again. So all is hopefully well there.

I finally feel that with kids, dog and parrot getting bored, it is time I stopped typing, for now at least.

All the above is why I became a vet. I love it. It is a great profession and I am proud to be part of it but, ultimately, it is the animals and the people that make it all worthwhile.